WAYNE E. OATES

ALCOHOL
IN AND OUT
OF THE CHURCH

BROADMAN PRESS
Nashville, Tennessee

to

Paul Ciholas
Richard Hester
Andrew Lester
Merval Rosa
Roy Woodruff

© 1966 • BROADMAN PRESS
Nashville, Tennessee
422-292
DEWEY DECIMAL CLASSIFICATION NUMBER: 178
Library of Congress Catalog Card Number: 66-15146
Printed in the United States of America
3.5N6513

Alcohol—In and Out of the Church

Acknowledgments

I am indebted to Dr. Foy Valentine, executive secretary of the Christian Life Commission of the Southern Baptist Convention, and to the members of the Commission for making it possible for me to state what things I feel Christians need to know and do in order to understand the problem of alcohol and alcoholism both within and without the context of the church.

Second, I appreciate the fellowship of a graduate seminar at Southern Baptist Theological Seminary, out of which have emerged the thoughts in this book. The following students, all Seminary degree candidates in the Department of Psychology of Religion and Pastoral Care, have collaborated in discussion, research, and the pastoral care of alcoholics in living situations: Paul Ciholas, Richard Hester, Andrew Lester, Merval Rosa, and Roy Woodruff. Mr. Woodruff has also coauthored chapter 6. All of us are in turn indebted to the medical staff of the Department of Social Work and the Department of Psychiatry at Louisville General Hospital. Especial thanks go to Dr. William Keller, chief of psychiatry at the Hospital and head of the Department of Psychiatry at the University of Louisville Medical School, and to John Frazier, who is in charge of the Social Work Department of the Psychiatric Division of Louisville General Hospital.

In a very real way this book is dedicated to the alcoholics and families of alcoholics whom we have counseled in the time of their stress. As Christian ministers, we have visited them, not just because they are alcoholics and "need our help," but because in them we find the revelation of God in Jesus Christ amid human suffering. We believe unequivocally that Jesus Christ has something to say to us through the alcoholic as well as something for us to say to the alcoholic.

Finally, I am indebted to Mrs. Richard Landon who has done the secretarial work in the preparation of this manuscript. Her competence is steadfast and unexcelled, and her dedication to this task has facilitated and accelerated its completion.

At the end of this work the reader will find a selected bibliography of books and journal articles that are basic to the understanding of the problems of alcohol and alcoholism.

WAYNE E. OATES
Louisville, Kentucky

their stress. As Christian ministers, we have visited them, not just because they are alcoholics and "need our help," but because in them we find the revelation of God in Jesus Christ amid human suffering. We believe unequivocally that Jesus Christ has something to say to us through the alcoholic as well as something for us to say to the alcoholic.

Finally, I am indebted to Mrs. Richard Landon who has done the secretarial work in the preparation of this manuscript. Her competence is steadfast and unexcelled, and her dedication to this task has facilitated and accelerated its completion.

At the end of this work the reader will find a selected bibliography of books and journal articles that are basic to the understanding of the problems of alcohol and alcoholism.

WAYNE E. OATES
Louisville, Kentucky

Acknowledgments

I am indebted to Dr. Foy Valentine, executive secretary of the Christian Life Commission of the Southern Baptist Convention, and to the members of the Commission for making it possible for me to state what things I feel Christians need to know and do in order to understand the problem of alcohol and alcoholism both within and without the context of the church.

Second, I appreciate the fellowship of a graduate seminar at Southern Baptist Theological Seminary, out of which have emerged the thoughts in this book. The following students, all Seminary degree candidates in the Department of Psychology of Religion and Pastoral Care, have collaborated in discussion, research, and the pastoral care of alcoholics in living situations: Paul Ciholas, Richard Hester, Andrew Lester, Merval Rosa, and Roy Woodruff. Mr. Woodruff has also coauthored chapter 6. All of us are in turn indebted to the medical staff of the Department of Social Work and the Department of Psychiatry at Louisville General Hospital. Especial thanks go to Dr. William Keller, chief of psychiatry at the Hospital and head of the Department of Psychiatry at the University of Louisville Medical School, and to John Frazier, who is in charge of the Social Work Department of the Psychiatric Division of Louisville General Hospital.

In a very real way this book is dedicated to the alcoholics and families of alcoholics whom we have counseled in the time of

Contents

I

What Alcohol Is and Does

We get our word for alcohol from the Arabic word *kuhl* or *kohol,* which means a fine powder. The word *Al-kohol* meant a very fine powder used as a cosmetic in darkening the eyelids. For a long time the word meant only that, but by the time of Paracelsus, a Swiss alchemist and physician who lived from 1493-1541, the word alcohol meant "essence." Paracelsus used it to refer to the subtle part or essence of wine: *alcool vini.* It was not until the nineteenth century that the word *vini,* Latin for wine, was dropped, and "alcohol" became a word that was used generally for wine spirits.

Alcohol is the physiologically active ingredient of intoxicating beverages. Alcohol is produced either by fermentation or distillation or both. The chemical formula for alcohol is C_2H_5O H. *The United States Pharmocopaeia* (adopted as standard for this country in the Food and Drugs Act of June 30, 1966, revised regularly by a committee of physicians and pharmacists, and used as the official standardizing manual in the field of drugs) speaks of absolute alcohol as having no more than 1 percent water. This is used for commercial purposes. Diluted alcohol (proof spirit) contains at least 41.42 percent alcohol by weight. The maximum amount of alcohol in wine is not much over 13 percent through the process of fermentation. However, wines may be "fortified" and thus contain more alcohol. Wine is fermented

1

from grapes and is usually a diluted solution of alcohol. Beer, obtained by the fermentation of a malted cereal such as barley, usually has from 3 to 5 percent alcohol content.

Whiskey, on the other hand, is not just a result of fermentation. It is a drinkable alcoholic liquor distilled from cereal grains. It gets its name from the Celtic *uisquebeatha*, later contracted to *usquebaugh*. This name means "the water of life." Whiskey is distilled spirits. The earliest known use of distillation as a means of producing alcohol is recorded in a twelfth century Latin manuscript, *Mappae Clavicula*, and it is safe to assume that alcohol was first produced by distillation in the wine districts of Italy about A.D. 1200. This is important information in our interpretation of the Scriptures. We wrongly assume that when the Bible mentions intoxicating beverages, it is referring to what we know today as whiskey. It is not. It is referring to fermented—not distilled—spirits. Fermented spirits run to about 13 percent alcohol content. The distilled spirits of whiskey run from 50 to 58 percent by weight. The Food and Drug Act of 1906 defines whiskey as "a distillate, at the required alcoholic strength, from the fermented mash of malted cereals, or from malt with unmalted cereals, and containing the congeneric substances formed with ethyl alcohol which are volatile at the ordinary temperature of distillation, and which gave the character of the distillate."

The importance of the distinction between fermentation and distillation becomes even more complex. Distillation was known and used as early as A.D. 1200. Nevertheless, it did not become generally used throughout Europe until the sixteenth and seventeenth centuries. Even then, it was an expensive process for the making of perfumes and rare and expensive whiskeys. These, because of expense, were not available to the poor. In the Industrial Revolution of the nineteenth and early twentieth centuries, however, distillation became an industry. By "industrial revolution" we mean the kind of social change which transforms an agricultural people with local markets into an industrial society of impersonally related people with worldwide markets. In this sense, the making of distilled spirits became something more than making "home brew" or "corn likker" in the backyard. Distilling became a major industry with an international market. Also, it brought the cost of alcoholic beverages within the reach of the poor man.

Consequently, easy comparisons between biblical and contemporary social conditions connected with alcohol—whether they be made by "dry" propagandists or "wet" propagandists—are confusing and less than helpful. Mass production and distribution, accompanied by mass techniques of advertising, have brought about an instruction in drinking and an availability of alcohol unknown before the Industrial Revolution—for people of all classes.

However, what has been said here about the movement of people to cities and the development of industries is not the whole story. Knowing the effects of urbanization and industrialization on the production of alcohol illuminates certain Old and New Testament attitudes about the use of alcohol. For example, neither the Rechabites nor the Nazirites drank strong drink nor ate any product of the vine (cf. Jer. 35:1-19; Num. 6:1-4; Judg. 13:5; Amos 2:11-12, RSV). One reason for this was that the vine was the symbol of a settled life and culture, of towns, cities, and earthly securities. The Nazirites and the Rechabites were bearing witness to "the old days" when the people of God were wanderers in the wilderness, pilgrims on earth, with no permanent abode. They were bearing witness to total dependence upon God rather than to dependence upon security derived from the amassing of wealth, the development of real estate holdings, or the inheritance of family property.

In contemporary life the structure of society has changed, and one of the hard realities of this change is that people in an industrial society are leaving the rural areas and moving to cities in order to work in industries. One of these industries is that of alcohol production.

What Alcohol Does

Now that we have a concise view of what alcohol is, we need to see what it does, particularly when used as a beverage.

When a person drinks an alcoholic beverage, the liquid enters the stomach and small intestine. Then it moves through the gastric and intestinal walls. It is carried by circulation through the liver to the heart. The heart distributes it by the systemic circulation to all parts of the body. Wherever alcohol touches bodily tissue, it has one effect: it serves as a depressant. This means that it retards or stops the function of any protoplasm upon which it acts directly. Protoplasm is the fundamental material of which all living things are composed. The chief component of protoplasm is water, which composes from 85 to 90 percent by weight of the average cell. The other constituents of protoplasm include proteins, fatty substances, and other organic substances such as carbohydrates.

Not all of the tissues of the body are affected to the same extent by alcohol.

The higher centers of the central nervous system are particularly sensitive to concentrations of alcohol much lower than the thresholds for other tissues such as muscle, glands, etc. It is for this reason that symptoms involving disturbances of thought processes, of mood, of sensation, and of coordination are among the first to appear after the ingestion of alcohol.[1]

It is common knowledge that the effects of alcoholic intoxication vary, as they do in any drug ingestion, with the amount of alcohol concentration in the bloodstream. These effects begin with changes in the thought and mood processes of the individual and continue with effects on speech and muscular coordination, pulse and respiration changes. As increasing amounts of alcohol are ingested, mental confusion, visual and auditory effects, and

---

[1] Robert E. Fleming, "On Certain Medical Aspects of Alcoholism," *Bulletin of the Academy of Medicine of New Jersey*, I, no. 3 (June 15, 1956), 14-15.

skin changes are also increased. Alcohol is poisonous to the organism

. . . because it is absorbed rapidly but is converted only slowly to carbon dioxide and water by way of acetaldehyde and acetic acid. The reported rates of conversion vary from 3.5 to 15 c.c. per hour. If absorbed at a faster rate than the rate at which it is metabolized, the alcohol content of the body fluids builds up and acts as a depressant on the nervous system. A concentration of around 0.2% results in moderate intoxication, 0.3% in severe intoxication, and 0.4% in deep anaesthesia which may be fatal.[2]

These percentages, one should observe, are percentage of concentration in the body fluids.

Obvious signs of intoxication appear in the average adult at about 0.25 percent of blood-alcohol concentration, the equivalent of twelve ounces of whiskey drunk within a few hours. Many people show evidence of intoxication at lower levels. The National Safety Council has adopted the concentration of 0.15 percent of alcohol in the blood as firsthand evidence of intoxication with respect to the operation of a motor vehicle.[3]

The amount of alcohol ingested by a person is not the only factor in intoxication. The rapidity with which he drinks the alcohol is a second factor. The degree of intoxication produced in a person depends not only on the concentration of alcohol in the blood and tissue fluids, but also on the rate at which this concentration is reached. "Numerous investigators have found that a subject is more intoxicated at a given blood-alcohol concentration if it is reached rapidly than if it is reached slowly; and he is much less intoxicated at a given concentration during the decline in blood-alcohol level after the peak is passed than during the early phase of rising blood-alcohol level."[4] This fact makes a

---

[2]C. Robert Nollin, "Alcohol," *The Encyclopaedia Britannica*, I (1959), 543.

[3]Arthur P. Noyes, *Modern Clinical Psychiatry* (4th ed.; Philadelphia: W. B. Saunders Company, 1953), pp. 185-86.

[4]H. Kalant, "The Pharmacology of Alcohol Intoxication," *Quarterly Journal of Studies on Alcohol*, Supplement 1 (November, 1961), p. 3.

basic difference in the patterns of alcohol drinking in different communities. For example, if alcohol is taken with meals (as is true in French and Italian communities) in small quantities, and over a leisurely period of time, then the degree of alcohol intoxication is considerably different from a situation in which a person at a bar or a cocktail party in America, prior to a meal and probably on an empty stomach, quickly drinks considerable amounts of alcohol in the form of whiskey and not in the form of beer or wine. The degree of intoxication produced in the first instance is far less serious than that produced in the second.

Effects on the Body

In an exhaustive study of the pharmacological effects of alcohol, Dr. Kalant identifies the main effects of alcohol intoxication on the human body. These are listed below.

Dietary effects.—Alcohol does not provide enough amounts of vitamins, minerals, or other dietary requirements to offset the straight calories it puts into the body. A human being can, theoretically, get more than two thousand calories in twenty-four hours from the use of alcohol at maximum rates. Therefore, other foods with their essential nutritional values simply are not eaten properly, if at all. This could be one reason why, in France, the alcoholic is considered to be the person who drinks alcohol at times other than meals and drinks whiskey rather than wine. The nutritional effects of alcohol upon the liver are seen medically as side effects. However, these side effects are exceptionally serious. In fact, some of the serious diseases related to vitamin deficiency are not direct effects, but a by-product of continued use of alcohol.

One of these diseases is Wernicke Syndrome. A syndrome is a group of signs or symptoms appearing in close association with one another, which usually identify a disease. The person suffering from this disease shows such symptoms as memory loss, clouding of consciousness, apathy, apprehension, and even coma. The main vitamin deficiency is thiamine, but there usually are other essential nutritional needs missing in the body.

Another vitamin deficiency disease associated with chronic alcohol deterioration is called Korsakoff's Syndrome. Strictly speaking, it is only a secondary result of, and not primarily caused by, use of alcohol. It results from a Vitamin B deficiency, a deficiency to which the chronic alcoholic who limits his diet largely to alcohol can fall prey. The symptoms which come with Korsakoff's disease are mainly memory defects, followed by an uncontrolled fabrication of stories to fill in the memory gap when questions are pressed upon the patient. On the surface the patient seems to be in contact with reality, to reason correctly, and to carry on seemingly coherent conversation. But closer inspection reveals that he is confused as to time and place of events. For example, an examiner knows that the patient has been in the hospital for weeks, and asks him: "Where were you last night?" Then the patient gives a detailed story of the places he went and the things he did the night before as if he were not in the hospital at all. On the same day, the same question asked later will be answered with a different story. The commonly used psychological name for this is *confabulation*. "Over a period of time, with good nutrition and polyvitamin therapy, confabulation may . . . show definite improvement." But if the memory defect is severe, complete restoration of the memory is unusual.[5]

Another dietary imbalance caused by alcohol's being too large a proportion of the total caloric intake is the accumulation of fat in the liver. We are told that the more recent "enrichment" or supplementation of flour, cereals, and other foods with vitamin supplement-vitamin additions has tended to offset this particular effect of alcoholism in recent years. However, the so-called fatty liver of the disease cirrhosis is still associated clinically with extensive alcohol intoxication over periods of time.

Neurological effects.—The part of the body most frequently affected by alcohol is the nervous system, primarily those mechanisms which regulate all the reflexes of the body. For example,

---

[5]*Alcoholism as a Medical Problem*, H. D. Kruse, ed. (New York: Hoeber-Harper, 1956), p. 86.

reaction time is affected in all persons, but not always in the same way. The introvert driving a car may become exceedingly cautious, while the extrovert will drive recklessly and with poor control. Alcohol exerts its first depressing action: integrating controls are lost, and various portions of the nervous system are left to their own devices. Thought processes occur in a jumbled, disorganized fashion. Thought content, emotional tone, and form of expression lose touch with reality, and alertness is diminished. The eyes develop a slow, rhythmical, rolling movement similar to those under intense heat and humidity.

The pleasant feeling of warmth induced by small amounts of alcohol can be a dangerous threat. Although the skin is flushed and sweating increases, the temperature of the more vital portions of the body falls. Consequently, the person under heavy alcoholic influences may be deceived by intensely cold weather. He may become overexposed and even freeze to death. The skid row alcoholic may be nearer death from serious frostbite or pneumonia than from the direct effects of alcohol.

Psychological effects.—One of the primary psychological effects of alcohol seems to be the *decrease of anxiety.* Several authorities have demonstrated that "there is no doubt that alcohol does have a tranquilizer-like effect and that it strongly potentiates or activates the action of tranquilizing drugs. When we later come to consider why people drink and how they learn to drink, we may well find some explanation of it as a kind of coping behavior in dealing with the problem of anxiety."[6]

Some sources of this anxiety have been identified from a developmental point of view. For example, anxiety has been traced to the pre-weaning stage of a child's life when his basic needs for security and complete dependence were unmet. This anxiety has been traced also to the later preschool years when the child lacked secure and trustworthy adults with whom he

---

[6] G. A. Zirkle *et al.,* "Meprobamate and Small Amounts of Alcohol: Effects on Human Ability, Coordination, and Judgment," *The Journal of the American Medical Association,* CLXXIII (1960), 1823-25.

might have identified as he developed his internal psychic controls. Furthermore, this anxiety has been traced to teen or adult years when harsh and legalistic patterns of hypermoralism were blindly applied and devoid of grace, mercy, and understanding.

Other psychologists have traced this anxiety to the kinds of stress created in the typical transitions that every person must make as he moves from one stage of his life to another. For example, as a man moves from the stage of childlessness along with his wife to the stage of parenthood, new stresses are laid upon him, new demands for responsibility are created, anxiety mounts. The same thing happens to women, for example, when all their children become old enough to be in public school or to have left the home for marriage, work, military service. One theory is that when these developmental tasks are faced, previously insignificant drinking of alcohol becomes intensely significant as a means of coping with anxiety.

One of the most common psychological effects of alcohol is the lowering or the *releasing of inhibition.* Through the narcotic action of alcohol on inhibitions, a person tends to feel that he can express himself more freely, act with more confidence and less uncertainty, with more ease and less self-restraint. His awareness of fatigue is dulled. As a result, he may think that his capabilities and powers of endurance have been greatly increased. The finer capacities of attention, judgment, comprehension, and reflection are dulled. This is implicitly significant from an ethical point of view. The inhibitions to performing morally unacceptable or socially inappropriate acts are removed. However, the capacity to perform those acts tends to be reduced along with the fear of the consequences of such acts.

For example, one common assumption is that alcohol makes a person more sexually violent, unscrupulous, and rapacious. But, the facts are that, whereas alcohol may increase the sexual drive or desire, the ability to be effective sexually is usually impaired. Jacob Levine studied this problem in seventy-nine cases and found that "the effects of alcohol upon the sex drive was by no means uniform." Seventy percent of his cases reported no sexual activity within a three-month period. Twenty-four percent of them reported no sexual activity in a whole year. Levine concluded that the reduction of the fear of one's sexual impulses might increase sexual interest, but that alcohol reduces the sexual competence of the person. Uncannily enough, this was exactly the poetic wisdom of Shakespeare in *Macbeth* when he said: "Lechery, sir, it [alcohol] provokes and unprovokes; it provokes the desire but takes away the performance. Therefore, much drink may be said to be an equivocation with lechery." The same thing could be said about other human drives. For example, one alcoholic said, "Alcohol made me a big man, and I thought I could rule the world when I was drunk. I painted the world with a huge brush and a few strokes!" In other words, alcohol increased his ambitions and his drives to mastery, but it decreased his capacity to implement these ambitions and/or to realize them.

One of the most common pathological results of ·advanced alcoholism is *delirium tremens,* commonly referred to as the "d.t.'s," "the shakes," and "the willies." This is rarely seen except in chronic alcoholics who have been drinking for a period of ten years or more. A long history of malnutrition usually precedes it, although inadequate nourishment is not the fault of a particular vitamin deficiency.

The disorder has a bizarre collection of nervous, psychological, and social aspects.

It usually begins with restlessness, irritability, insomnia, and terrify-ing nightmares. Within 24 hours, there is a progression of the disorder to the point where the patient shows clouding of consciousness and disorientation for time, place, and person. Attention is poor, comprehension is difficult, and thought processes are frequently illogical. These difficulties are usually worse at night and upon awakening from a sleep. Vivid, visual hallucinations and illusions are the most common type of perceptual disorder. Small dark colored animals, such as rats, dogs, and snakes are described with a characteristic emotional reaction of terror and fear. The persecutory delusions add to the apprehension and fright. In addition, the patient shows mistrust, suspicion, and uncertainty. There is a coarse tremor of the hands, tongue, and face. . . . The illness usually runs its course in three or four days unless a complication like pneumonia sets in.[7]

Although we have not seen all that alcohol is and can do to and for a human being, we have identified some of the major critical issues. The next step is to study the processes whereby we learn to use alcohol as human beings.

The Prevalence of Drinking

A specific understanding of the prevalence of the drinking of alcohol as a beverage is now needed. For a long time religious literature has treated drinking as if there were no differences between the drinking patterns of different people. This literature has led churches to misunderstand the issues in alcohol education and therefore to mistreat and fail to redeem the person who is an alcoholic. A helpful study by Harold A. Mulford, a sociologist at the University of Iowa, presents the wide spectrum of different patterns of drinking and provides a realistic understanding of the prevalence and nature of drinking among Americans.[8] Mulford has studied the prevalence of drinkers, nondrinkers, ex-drinkers, and "deviant" drinkers in the national population according to the various selected segments of the population. The "deviant" drinker was the one who consumed larger quantities of alcohol more frequently and, as a result, had trouble on his job, in his marriage, in overspending on alcohol, in running afoul of the law through drunkenness and illegal driving habits, in injuring his health. Incidentally, among these various indications of deviant or abnormal drinking, the most frequent expressions of complaint concerned money spent

---

[7]S. Mouchly Small, quoted in *Alcoholism as a Medical Problem*, H. D. Kruse (ed.), p. 84.

[8]"Drinking and Deviant Drinking, U.S.A., 1963" *Quarterly Journal of Studies on Alcohol*, XXV, No. 4 (December, 1964), 634-50.

for alcohol, injury to health, and trouble with the police—in that order.

Eighty million Americans drink alcohol to some extent. This is 71 percent of the population. E. M. Jellinek, the foremost authority on alcoholism, estimates that 4,470,000 men and 710,000 American women are alcoholics.[9] Persons living in urbanized and industrialized states, such as the Middle Atlantic states, drink at a higher percentage of 88 percent, which is two and one-half times greater than the East South Central states of 38 percent. These are more rural and less industrialized areas. The prevalence of drinking is greater among men than women, greatest between the ages of twenty-one and thirty-nine. Drinking is more common among Jews, Catholics, and Lutherans, more common among single persons than married ones. Drinking is more prevalent among the educated than the uneducated, among the higher income brackets and upper occupational groups. These facts point to the possibility that, as a community becomes more depersonalized and as individuals move upward on the social ladder, the prevalence of drinking increases.

Among religious groups, the highest rate of heavy drinkers appears in Protestants who do not specify a denomination, and the lowest rates appear among Methodists, Baptists, and Jews. Jews have the lowest number, probably because of their close family ties and their ceremonially restricted use of alcohol. However, the persons who experience the greatest difficulties in adjustment because of drinking tend to be Baptists or members of smaller, close-knit religious sects. This points to the possibility that while the more tightly knit religious community tends to eliminate the habit of drinking, it tends at the same time to isolate and ostracize the drinker, making drinking more compulsive. Yet, Mulford also demonstrates that when a particular segment of the population has a low rate of drinkers, that segment

---

[9]Vera Efron and Mark Keller, *Selected Statistical Tables on the Consumption of Alcohol and on Alcoholism* (New Brunswick, N. J.: Journal of Studies on Alcohol, 1963), p. 3.

is the most successful in motivating drinkers to abandon their drinking.

The minister or layman who seeks to understand and cope with the problem of alcohol has another dilemma to contend with. Statistics show that people living in the South Atlantic, East South Central, and West South Central portions of the United States are the most abstinent persons in the country. Here, five out of ten adults drink alcohol to some extent, as compared with nine out of ten in the industralized northeastern portions of the country. Despite the difference in the percentage of drinkers, those in the southern areas have more problems with deviant drinking. This fact suggests the need for a different approach to the problem of alcohol, both in and out of the church. We need to see how drinking causes trouble, how the trouble can be handled, and finally how it can be prevented. Many Protestants have moved against alcohol and alcoholism; but we need to add to our zeal knowledge and insight. The prayer with which this book is written asks this for both author and reader.

II

How We Learn to Drink Alcohol

Drinking alcohol is learned behavior, not inherited knowledge. Any realistic program of alcohol education or plan for controlling the use of alcohol requires careful study of how and why people learn to drink. This knowledge should undergird our understanding of people who misuse alcohol.

The problem of alcohol is complicated by conflicting views held by various religious and cultural groups. In the United States many Baptists, Methodists, and members of smaller religious groups have strongly opposed any use of alcoholic beverages. This viewpoint has been reinforced by the teaching that drinking is sinful and must not be tolerated. On the other hand, European Christians usually have not held this view. American branches of the large church groups of Europe—such as Catholics, Lutherans, and Episcopalians—ordinarily have not opposed moderate drinking. To many members of these groups, complete opposition to alcohol does not appear to be a Christian virtue. Rather it seems to be an unchristian kind of bigotry.

For the present, let us see these views merely as facts that complicate any Christian approach to the problem of drinking. They are part of the background that we must recognize and understand. They are part of the insight that is required in order to deal with alcohol. We would do well to follow the advice of the biblical writer: "The beginning of wisdom is this: Get wisdom,

14

and whatever you get, get insight. Prize her highly, and she will exalt you; she will honor you if you embrace her" (Prov. 4:7, RSV).

Drinking As Learned Behavior

One of the first superstitions we must fell in our attempt to understand and cope with alcohol and alcoholism as a social problem is that easy scapegoat of bad heredity. This widely held idea complicates rather than relieves the distress of the family of the alcoholic, multiplies unnecessarily the burden of guilt the alcoholic is bearing already, and creates hindrances in growth for the children of alcoholics.

We need to know what we are talking about when we say that a particular habit or trait is inherited. Heredity is the transmission of characteristics from parent to offspring. These characteristics are determined at conception and not at birth. Even the events that occur between the time the child is conceived and the time it is born are not considered hereditary but congenital. A disposition toward alcoholism is not inherited. Rather, a constitution involving such general personality "instability as does not offer sufficient resistance to the social risks or inebriety" may provide a breeding ground for inebriety, according to E. M. Jellinek.[1]

Jellinek points out that this liability itself exists in only 35 percent of those who do become alcoholic. This percentage does not justify the assumption that inebriety is largely dependent upon what has been called "non-specific heredity."

Ten years after Jellinek reported his research, M. D. Sherfey studied 165 patients at Payne Whitney Clinic in New York. She concluded that the "simple symptom of pathological drinking would originate from relationships with the alcoholic relative rather than from a constitutional (or hereditary) origin."[2]

---

[1] "Heredity of the Alcoholic," *Alcohol, Science, and Society* (New Haven: *Quarterly Journal of Studies on Alcoholism,* 1945), p. 109.

[2] O. Diethelm (ed.), *The Etiology of Chronic Alcoholism,* (Springfield, Ill.: Thomas, 1955), pp. 16-42.

About the same time, R. J. Williams pointed out that genetic differences in nutritional needs might indirectly involve the craving for alcohol. However, these are secondary effects and not primary results of heredity.[3]

We are safe in concluding that it is impossible to separate hereditary and environmental factors in the histories of alcoholics that have been studied in considerable numbers over a period of time. There is no real evidence that alcoholism in parents causes mental disorders in the offspring. The genetics of alcoholism are usually confused with the genetics of other personality problems of which alcoholism is only one expression. This should be a comfort as well as a challenge to the family of an alcoholic person.

This evidence plus much more that could be cited leads me to the conclusion that alcohol consumption is learned behavior. It is learned and it can be taught, but it is not inherited in the clear sense of what heredity means. There may be congenital and postnatal effects of parental alcoholism, but heredo-alcoholism, as it is called, does not exist.[4]

Drinking Reduces Drives

Drinking is a learned response to the demands of human drives. Each of us has a complex patterning of cooperative and conflicting drives, desires, or needs. We hunger. We thirst. We get angry. We become aroused sexually. We appeal for attention and approval from others. We become frightened and anxious. The drinking response in the use of alcohol is learned because it in one way or another reduces these different drives. When drinking rewards us in the reduction of these drives, then we drink again. At the outset, we learn to drink because in some way or another it is rewarding to us.

---

[3]"The Genotrophis Concept, Nutritional Deficiencies, and Alcoholism," *Annal of the New York Academy of Sciences*, LVII (1954), 794-809.

[4]L. Christiaens, J. P. Mizon, and G. Delmarle, "On the Offspring of Alcoholics," *Annals Pediatrique*, XXXVI (1960), 37-46.

If this working hypothesis for how we learn to drink is useful, we have a right to ask this question: Which of our needs or drives is reduced most by the drinking of alcohol? John J. Conger says that drinking alcohol reduces the strength of fear and/or anxiety. This, to him, is the drive often and most completely reduced by the use of alcohol.

Hunger Drive.—A part of the answer to this question can be found in studying the hunger drive. Roger J. Williams studied alcohol and nutrition at the Biochemical Institute of Texas University for eleven years. In that time he demonstrated—to his coworkers' satisfaction and with considerable success in the treatment of alcoholics—that one basic cause of alcoholism is nutritional deficiency and that the alcoholic's behavior is learned as a response to this deficiency. He worked on the assumption that the behavior could be unlearned by correcting the nutritional deficiency. However, the nutritional deficiency in the instance of the alcoholic is too great to be compensated for simply by modifying the person's normal diet. For example, in the case of Vitamin B, *"There is no food source rich enough to supply generous amounts of all."* Williams suggested that the following complex of vitamin-supplement be administered to the alcoholic on a daily basis:

Thiamine	3.3	mg.
Riboflavin	2.67	mg.
Nicotinamide	10	mg.
Calcium pantothenate	10	mg.
Pyridoxin	3.3	mg.
Biotin	0.05	mg.
Folic acid	1.1	mg.
p-Aminobenzoic acid	11	mg.
Inositol	53	mg.
Choline	53	mg.
Vitamin B_{12}	5	g.
Vitamin A	6,667	units
Vitamin C	33.3	mg.
a-Tocopherol	6.67	mg.
Viosterol	333	units

It is advised that three capsules be taken daily for the first week. If there are no contraindications, six capsules daily (two with each meal) should be taken the next week, and if there are still no contra-indications, nine capsules daily (taken with meals) the third week and as long thereafter as may be indicated.[5]

Williams freely admits that this is only a partial explanation of alcohol addiction, and that the vitamin therapy will succeed in some instances and not in others. I should think that the length of time the person has been addicted to alcohol will have something to do with the measure of success. As we have already seen, some of the dietary effects of alcohol consumption go beyond the point of no return and are irreversible even when arrested. However, the nutritional theory of how we learn to drink, it seems to me, will inevitably be a part of understanding and dealing with problems associated with the use of alcohol.

Drive of fear.—Further, alcohol reduces the strength of our drive to run, retreat, or be afraid. We may be afraid of our own tempers, our own sexual temptations, our own desire to be out-going and related to other people. In any of these instances, however, the reduction of the fear and anxiety created by these unacceptable impulses will make an agent of reduction such as alcohol useful and rewarding. If it is useful and rewarding often enough, then the habit structure of drinking is set. We are on our way to becoming habituated.[6]

This is to oversimplify the causes of fear and anxiety, how-ever; for the reduction of fear and anxiety in one area produces the contrary effect on our interpersonal competence. Whether it is in the sphere of sexual behavior, in the expression of hostility toward an opponent, or in the capture of the attention and affection of someone who has rejected us, the performance of our total being is reduced along with the

---

[5]*Nutrition and Alcoholism* (Norman, Okla.: University of Oklahoma Press, 1951), p. 38.

[6]John J. Conger, "Reinforcement Theory and the Dynamics of Alcohol-ism," *Quarterly Journal of Studies on Alcoholism*, XVII (1956), 296-305.

fear. The drives which are inhibited by fear are short-circuited through the use of alcohol. Instead of mobilizing human strength in the constructive use of these great drives, alcohol immobilizes and gives undirected expression to the same human strength. The total personality is stalemated. This immobilization can and does become the alcoholic's way of life.

The road to becoming an alcoholic, however, is an unsure one. Not all people who drink become alcoholics, and not all who say they can drink without becoming alcoholics manage to do so. Some church members tend to think of anyone who drinks as exactly like everyone else who drinks. Yet we believe in the significance of the individual, and it thus behooves each of us to look closely at the individual differences in drinking patterns.

Drink and the Community

Harold Fallding, a visiting associate professor of sociology at the Rutgers Center of Alcohol Studies in New Brunswick, New Jersey, has wisely associated the use of alcohol with the kind of relationship the drinker has to his own spiritual community or "kin group." A kin group seeks to sponsor a common life through basic institutions of the home, the church, the school, and so on. The kin group develops a unique way of life. Members of the group jealously guard this way of life or "culture." They live together both to survive and to flourish. They cannot survive unless they can maintain mutual trust. Yet, many of the things they produce are not necessary to their survival. Many things serve only as adornments and ornaments of their life together. A frontier church, for example, can survive in a brush arbor if mutual trust and love sustain the people in hope. A large suburban church also can survive if it has this, even if it does have expensive carpeting, pews, and chandeliers. But these ornaments do not create a church. A family, for example, can survive with bread, meat, milk, vegetables, clothing, and a shack for a house, *if* it has mutual trust and if love sustains its members in hope. A home can survive with air conditioning, gourmet food, two cars in the garage, and expensive as well as necessary clothing, if it has mutual trust and if love sustains it in hope. But these luxuries can break as well as bind a home.

The basic issue of a community or a civilization, then, is the burden of putting the ornaments of life to an innocent use, according to Fallding. Oxygen, for example, is an indispensable necessity or condition of life. We have no moral rules about the use of oxygen. But alcohol is not a necessity for life; it is either an innocently or destructively used ornament, a surplus of society that must be used in one way or another. We must then have a morality about alcohol.

The ways people use alcohol are the bases for Fallding's classification of four different kinds of drinking. The fear of alienation and estrangement from the community is the negative drive; the need for trust and security in the fellowship of the community is the positive drive in this typology of drinking.

1. *Ornamental or Community-Symbolic Drinking.* Fallding says that ornamental drinking "symbolizes preexisting community." For example, in the early church, wine was drunk as a part of the meal (cf. 1 Cor. 11:21-22). The people of the church apparently not only ate too much but drank too much as well. Paul asked that the community of faith, hope, and love, symbolized in the Lord's Supper, be focused upon the death, burial, and resurrection of Jesus Christ in the fellowship of the church, the preexisting community which caused them "to come together in one place." Here, wine was used to express an already existing relationship, not to generate a relationship that did not previously exist. Drinking here symbolizes "the most precious support men can experience."

Another example of this kind of drinking is the family meal of the German, the French, or the Italian family. They drink as a part of the common bond of fellowship within the family. For example, Albert D. Ullman studied Jewish, Italian, and Chinese habits of drinking in comparison with Americans who have no particular ethnic background other than an Anglo-Saxon

American culture. He demonstrated that the outstanding feature, for example, of the drinking patterns of the Italian is the use of wine with meals. Jews drink in connection with religious ceremonies as well as with meals. Chinese drink on all occasions of eating, but not at other times. The incidence of alcoholism in these cultures is much lower than in a group or society in which drinking is inconsistent with the rest of culture.

This may sound as though I am suggesting that a culture such as that of the Southern states would have less alcoholism if everyone drank. Far from it. It points to the fact that when a church member in such a culture takes up the habit of drinking, he alienates himself from his accustomed and accepted community. Therefore, he is more likely to become alcoholic through social drinking than would a Jew, an Italian, or an Italian-American. This could be one of the reasons why the World Health Organizattion has defined alcoholism as "any form of drinking which in its extent goes beyond the traditional and customary 'dietary' use, or the ordinary compliance with the social drinking customs of the whole community concerned, . . ."[7]

However, the tragedy of American life is what Fallding calls the "eclipse of community among us." In an industrial and urban society such as our own, life is depersonalized and mechanized. In such a society we use alcohol in an attempt to reinstate a community artificially "in advance of the restoration of real community." Fallding says:

> We see what only amounts to a travesty of it [community] in those who go to their drinking, and impose the enjoyment of it on others, as if it were a hanging. This is illustrated in the practice of trying to create community by setting up attractive bars instead of stirring people up to faith and love. But nothing could be less sufficient for the genesis of community than to supply the materials by which it could be symbolized if present.[8]

---

[7]World Health Organization Technical Report Series, No. 42, 1951.

[8]"The Source and Burden of Civilization Illustrated in the Use of Alcohol," *Quarterly Journal of Studies on Alcohol*, XXV, No. 4 (December, 1964), 718-19.

2. *Facilitation Drinking.* This kind of drinking is done by a person who has trouble becoming a part of his community even though he trusts it, identifies with it, and is accepted by it. Drinking eases the adjustment of the person to his social group. This person has internal barriers to community with other people. He cannot participate without anesthetizing the fears which come from within himself. This is "alcohol-aided courage." However, alcohol may have a double effect: While it eases his fears, softens his grief, and reduces his tensions, it also releases his hostilities.

This double effect of facilitative drinking is the source of the controversies we find among religious people about social drinking. One group of people will say that social drinking is the negation of alcoholism, that social drinking rewards the company of drinkers with one another's companionship.[9] Alcohol is viewed by this group as a part of the creation and should not be rejected but "received with thanksgiving" (1 Tim. 4:4). "A Christian who drinks moderately with due regard for the feelings and needs of his brothers and with a conscientious care for the claims of God can drink with thanksgiving to him for these blessings."[10] However, his temptation will be to drink in order to gain the approval of men rather than of God.

Other Christian groups look on the darker side of facilitative or social drinking. These groups move to total abstinence on the basis of such Bible teachings as 1 Corinthians 8 and Romans 14:21. They believe that their drinking offends those who have been or may be hurt by alcohol.

Add to religious groups the large number of skilled workers who abstain for occupational or safety reasons, and the number of ambitious penny-wise people who do not drink because it is a luxury that can be foregone, and you have considerable numbers with good reasons for abstinence.

---

[9]*Alcohol, Alcoholism, and Social Drinking: An Official Publication of the Joint Commission on Alcoholism of the Protestant Episcopal Church in the United States of America* (Greenwich, Conn., 1958), p. 13.
[10]*Ibid.,* p. 21.

But the temptation of the total abstainer is to use his abstinence as a means of gaining social approval. This is no different from the person who uses social drinking to gain acceptance into his group. In both instances, acceptance into that community whose approval one considers more worthwhile, and survival as a member of that community, is "facilitated," to use Fallding's term, either by drinking or not drinking.

3. *Assuagement Drinking.* Here, alcohol becomes a substitute for a community of mutual trust and common purpose. Uprooted, lonely people seek substitutes for companionship. Being fulfilled in fellowship is replaced by having one's fill of something. Alcohol is only one of the substitutes. Fallding lists many:

> Food (compulsive eating and overweight are addictive, too), sex, possessions, distinctions, power, information, notoriety, mystical exaltations, drugs, jazz, tobacco, alcoholic titillation or intoxication. The experiences are taken raw. They are stripped of the meanings with which they are customarily invested by institutional contexts which make them a different thing. The filling is needed to block out the awareness that one is out of society: the compulsion for it stems, presumably, from the unrelievable emptiness. . . . Where else could we classify, for instance, the peculiar glazed encounter at cocktail parties, of strangers, rivals, enemies, deceivers? Bad faith, the supreme sacrilege in the eyes of those who drink to celebrate community symbolically, presents itself here very thinly veiled.[11]

This kind of drinking assuages temporarily the utter loneliness and meaninglessness of life. The immediacy and transitoriness of the satisfaction, however, produces a burden of guilt and unfulfilment along with its momentary satisfaction. Tennessee Williams describes a cocktail party in much the same terms:

> . . . *not meaning* overhangs these affairs like the cloud of cigarette smoke and the hectic chatter. All social functions involving a group of people not intimately known to each other are always under this shadow.[12]

---

[11] Fallding, *op. cit.*, pp. 720-21.
[12] *Rose Tattoo* (New York: New Directions Books, 1951), p. 8.

What he says of a New York cocktail party could as easily be said of many "receptions," "teas," and "banquets" held by total abstainers from alcohol. The food, the angling for position, the clothes, the titles, the positions mentioned, and so forth become tattered and temporary substitutes for real community among people who genuinely care what happens to one another.

Assuagement drinking is what makes drinking uncontrollable. Here, voluntary control is lost. The whole life of the person is geared to drinking when he is cut loose from or refused admission by his meaningful community. This is one thing that makes the difference between the 80,000,000 Americans and the 4,470,000 alcoholics, 12,000 of whom died each year as a result of the effects of alcohol. The World Health Organization defines the alcoholic in terms of the "overpowering desire or need (compulsion) to take alcohol and to take it by any means." Furthermore, according to this report, alcoholism is a psychic (psychological) and sometimes physical dependence on the effects of alcohol.[13]

4. *Retaliation Drinkers.* Fallding classifies alcoholics as assuagement drinkers or *retaliation* drinkers. The retaliation drinker is not only psychically or psychologically dependent upon alcohol as a drug, but he also "exploits the incapacitating power of alcohol in order to make himself a passenger on the system" of the community which he distrusts. Whereas facilitation drinking enables the person to lay aside his fear and become a part of the community, retaliation drinking activates the hostilities in such a way as to set the drinker against the community but make him dependent upon it.

Fallding points out, however, that these outcasts "can make a wistful, paradoxical case, insofar as they create traces of community among themselves; the same drinking as effects their rejection of others, symbolizes a flickering acceptance of one another."[14]

---

[13]World Health Organization Technical Report Series, No. 21 (1950), p. 6.

[14]Fallding, *op. cit.*, p. 721.

The facilitative drinker can be thought of as the social drinker. The assuagement drinker can be thought of as the problem drinker. The retaliative drinker can be thought of as the alcoholic. E. M. Jellinek studied the phases in the drinking history of a thousand alcoholics who achieved a measure of sobriety through Alcoholics Anonymous. The movement away from and back to the community is evident in these histories. Apart from a return to community, deterioration and death set in.

Alcoholism moves through definable phases of prealcoholic or "prodromal" symptoms, acute symptoms, chronic symptoms, and either recovery or deterioration and death. The earliest age of these persons reaching the lowest point of their career as alcoholics was reached just before forty years of age. Judged by first admissions of alcoholics to hospitals for treatment, alcoholism as a disease is developed between ages forty-five and fifty-five.

Alcoholics Anonymous is an experiment in community, a group approach to creating a subcivilization for reversing the processes described by Fallding and their symptoms as described by Jellinek. The early explorers in group therapy coined a maxim: "By the crowd have they been broken, by the crowds shall they be healed." This is the assumption and working hypothesis of the AA groups. Further discussion of their work will be included in the later chapter on conversion and recovery. Suffice it to say here that the ingredients of a healthy community—symbolic creation of a trust and realistic acceptance—are reintroduced here to defeat the power of alcohol over their lives. Whereas drinking became a means of assuagement and retaliation, now *not* drinking engenders confidence and hope instead. The group itself takes over the job of facilitating the alcoholic's fear and anxiety amid the committed AAs. The "coffee klatches" of AA become an adornment of a preexisting community of trust. The question that the member or pastor of a local church must of necessity ask is this: "What is the quality of fellowship, trust, and hope evident in my church?" This may be a clue to a creative offense against alcoholism rather than a negative defense.

From a developmental point of view, then, alcoholism must be seen as a "progressive disease, which, if untreated, grows more virulent year by year, driving its victims further and further from the normal world, and deeper and deeper into an abyss which has only two outlets: insanity and death."[15]

When we say, however, that alcoholism is a disease, we mean that certain kind of drinking which has passed the point of no return and which the alcoholic no longer can control. We do not mean that the alcholic is not morally responsible for his own situation before his neighbors and before God. He is responsible. He bears the brunt, not only of his own wrong choices, but also those of his family and society. He is morally responsible, but not he *alone* is morally responsible. He *is* a man of unclean lips, but he also lives in the midst of a people of unclean lips.

Kinds of Alcoholism

E. M. Jellinek, by identifying various kinds of alcoholism, summarizes the ways in which persons learn to drink. Lumping all alcoholics into one classification ignores the fact that differing kinds of alcoholism have different individual or social causes. Jellinek uses the Greek alphabet to designate these types according to something of a psychophysical continuum, classifying them according to functional causes and symptoms. The Greek letters are used to avoid terms with unfavorable connotations. I am indebted to Richard Hester for the following outline and chart, which summarize briefly these forms of alcoholism.

1. *Alpha alcoholism:*
   Purely a psychological continual dependence upon the effect of alcohol to relieve body or emotional pain
   a. Drinking is "undisciplined"—contravening rules of society
   b. Does not lead to "loss of control" or "inability to abstain"
   c. No withdrawal symptoms

---

[15]Marty Mann, *New Primer on Alcoholism* (New York: Holt, Rinehart, and Winston, 1958), p. 1.

    d. Damage to interpersonal relations, family budget, productivity
    e. This "undisciplined drinking" is symptomatic of pathological condition it relieves; therefore, the drinking cannot be regarded as an illness *per se*.
    f. Only occasionally progresses to *gamma* type

2. *Beta alcoholism:*
Alcoholism in which there is physiological dependence on alcohol without physical or psychological dependence on alcohol
    a. Incentive to drink is due to social custom in connection to nutritional problems
    b. Does not lead to "loss of control" or "inability to abstain"
    c. No withdrawal symptoms
    d. Damage to health, budget, productivity, life span
    e. The illness involved is damage to overall health and not that of addiction
    f. Only occasionally progresses to *gamma* type

3. *Gamma alcoholism:*
Alcoholism in which there is physiological dependence on alcohol with loss of control over the amount ingested during any one drinking period
    a. Incentive to drink—progression from psychological dependence to physiological dependence (addiction)
    b. Leads to loss of control; ability to abstain retained
    c. Withdrawal symptoms
    d. Physiological characteristics:
        (1) Increased tissue tolerance for alcohol
        (2) Adaptive cell metabolism
        (3) Withdrawal syndrome
    e. Psychological characteristics: marked behavior change
    f. Regarded as a disease
    g. Damage to interpersonal relations, health, budget, social standing
    h. This kind of alcoholism dominant in U.S. and Canada; most AA members of this type

4. *Delta alcoholism:*
Alcoholism in which there is physiological dependence on alcohol with inability to abstain from ingestion of alcohol for any period of time
    a. Incentive to drink—progression from social custom or psychological dependence to physiological dependence (addiction)

Type	Addictive Pattern	Socio-Economic Factors	Physiological Dynamics
Alpha	Psychological craving without physiological addiction (can progress to gamma type)	Purely a dependence on alcohol to relieve psychological or physical pain	No withdrawal reaction; not regarded as a symptom of psychological pathology
Beta	Psychological craving without physiological addiction (can progress to gamma type)	Drinking pattern probably reinforced by social custom	No withdrawal reaction; not regarded as a disease
Gamma	Psychological craving leads to physiological addiction	Most typical of Canada and U.S. alcoholism; supported by (1) availability of highly concentrated alcohol and (2) social custom	(1) Increased tolerance; (2) adaptive cell metabolism; (3) withdrawal symptoms and physiological dependence Regarded as a disease
Delta	Psychological craving or social custom leads to physiological addiction	Most typical of vitacultural countries; supported by (1) availability of low-concentration alcohol and (2) social custom	(1) Increased tolerance; (2) adaptive cell metabolism; (3) withdrawal symptoms and physiological dependence Regarded as a disease
Epsilon	Psychological craving is primary	(Little information available)	(Little information available)

Characteristic Drinking Pattern	Influence on Behavior	Resultant Damage
Undisciplined continual drinking without loss of control or inability to abstain	Alcoholism is a manifestation of other problem	Interpersonal relationships, family budget, declining productivity
Undisciplined continual drinking without loss of control or inability to abstain	Behavior changes secondary to physical damage	Physical disease without physiological dependence is the salient characteristic of this type
Reduction of undisciplined drinking; dependence on alcohol with loss of control; ability to abstain retained	Extensive behavior changes (most AA members in this type)	Interpersonal relationships, family budget, declining productivity, social standing
Uninterrupted dependence on alcohol—inability to abstain; ability to control is retained	Limited behavior changes	Health problem and shortening of life span is primary damage
Episodic drinking		

    b. Leads to inability to abstain; ability to control the amount ingested is retained
    c. Withdrawal symptoms
    d. Physiological characteristics:
        (1) Increased tissue tolerance for alcohol
        (2) Adaptive cell metabolism
        (3) Withdrawal syndrome
    e. Psychological characteristics: limited behavior change
    f. Regarded as a disease
    g. Damage to health and life span
    h. This kind of alcoholism is dominant in vitacultural countries (eg. France); few AA members of this type

5. *Epsilon alcoholism:*

Alcoholism which is periodic; little known about this type; "pseudo-periodic" alcoholic is the *gamma* type which abstains for a long period of time[16]

---

[16]E. M. Jellinek, *The Disease Concept of Alcoholism* (New Haven: Hill-house Press, 1960), pp. 36-41.

III

Drinking Patterns and Social Class

> *He who excels in beauty, strength,*
> *birth, or wealth, or on the other hand is*
> *very poor, or very weak, or very much*
> *disgraced, finds it difficult to follow ra-*
> *tional principle.*
>
> ARISTOTLE, *Politics*

Since the writings of Aristotle, attempts have been made to understand the irrational behavior of people in terms of their station in life, their social class. A person's particular social class provides him with or deprives him of fellowship with his own kind. Whether this is the way things *should* be, it is the way they are. The pastor and religious worker must both understand and cope with this reality. It is not enough to curse the darkness. One must light a candle of understanding if he is to cope with the things that provide a sense of community.

The previous chapter has been built upon the thesis that drinking either happens in a community with understood meanings, symbols, and rituals, or it happens in isolation with meaninglessness and compulsion. Fellowship is one of the intentions of the church. Loneliness and isolation are its competitors. Meaning, purpose, and calling are the meat and bread of the fellowship of believers known as the church. Emptiness, purposelessness, and compulsive commitment to alcohol, possessions, power, distinction, sexual irresponsibility, and so forth are the husks to which people starved for meaning and purpose go for satiation, not satisfaction.

In contemporary American life, much loneliness and emptiness

31

grows out of the ways in which Americans can move freely from one part of the country to another (horizontal mobility) and from one level of social status in a given community to another (vertical mobility). Loneliness and emptiness in people's lives occur on a massive scale when industry, the building of cities, famine, prosperity, and war cause extensive and complicated movement of people from the farms, villages, and small towns of their births. (As has already been seen, drinking is more than twice as extensive in the industrialized areas of the United States as it is in the rural areas of the country.)

Furthermore, the loneliness in people's lives becomes intensely personal when, through education, economic success, and movement up the social ladder, they come to the point that they no longer are "at home" with their families and home church. For example, in a study of alcoholic psychoses in the general population of Texas, E. Gartly Jaco points out that alcohol psychoses among Anglo-American men appeared two and one-half times more frequently among those with a college education than among those with no education. Among Spanish-American men, alcohol psychoses appeared seven times more frequently among those with a college education than among those with no education. Unimaginative reading of these data would cause one to jump at the conclusion that education *caused* the alcoholism. But when one imagines the separation, isolation, and loneliness produced by a college education in the life of a Mexican from a border town, one sees alcoholism as a husk of comfort to the alienated person. Drinking and alcoholism are symptoms of the failure of the intact spiritual community to meet the needs of all its members, and by-products of the estrangement of individuals from their families.

Churches have entered the field of education with force. Young people are moving up out of the lower classes and into the middle and upper classes both by education and by economic success. As they do so, the social standards about drinking which they confront are very different from those of their parents and grandparents. Drinking customs are only one set of customs that differ from those of their childhood. Protestants committed to education are obliged to bridge the gaps of culture which education brings into the lives of the educated. This cannot be done without an understanding of social class differences. Protestants committed to a pattern of success in church building and movement to the suburbs of large cities are obligated to bridge the gaps created by the economic success enjoyed by the affluent suburbanite. This cannot be done without an understanding of social class differences.

Different social classes differ in their attitudes toward drinking. The purpose of this chapter is to explore these attitudes to see what their effects upon people may be.

What Determines Social Class

A popular assumption is that social class is an indication of one's wealth. But this is a threadbare misunderstanding of what is meant technically by social class. The subtle technicalities are more difficult to discuss in groups or in public than sex itself. They are almost as difficult to discuss as is the subject of prayer at many respectable social gatherings! But talk about them we must, and understanding them calls for asking this question: What is a social class and what determines it? The answers to this question may permit us better to evaluate our social situations, deal with social reality, and understand the ways in which alcohol fits into the dreams, aspirations, and frustrations of people moving from one social class to another.

A social class is a portion of the total community structure of people who fill social roles defined by the kind of work they do, their length of stay as a family in the community, the amount of money and goods they own and produce, the location and quality of their places of residence, and the customs, mores, and values by which they live. As W. Lloyd Warner has said, "When societies are complex and service large populations, they always possess some kind of status system which, by its own values, places people in higher or lower positions."² This happens because of the efforts of a community to coordinate the efforts of its members, preserve the community as a whole, and maintain and perpetuate its identity as a community proudly and hopefully in touch with its heritage and its goals.

In this definition can be found several "status characteristics" which determine a person's social class:

1. *Education.*—This involves both the amount of education he has—grade school, high school, college, professional—and the quality of school from which he received it. For example, an education from a parochial, private, or public school, or from a denominational, state university, or an "Ivy League" school would differ.

2. *Occupation.*—This involves not only the kind of work a person does but also the connection that work has with his family heritage. For example, a person can be a doctor and hold one position in the community, but if he comes from a "long line" of doctors 'in the family," this provides a kind of seniority prestige.

3. *Income.*—This involves not only the amount of income, but also its source. For example, income from salary and from stocks, bonds, etc., represent two different classes of income. Also, money that is inherited may be no more in quantity than that of the "newly rich," but those who are of a tradition of wealth are in a different class from those who are not.

4. *Associations.*—This refers to clubs, organizations, memberships, etc., in which a person participates. Church membership is one of these. Civic clubs, country clubs, professional organizations, and so forth are others.

5. *Location of Dwelling.*—This refers to one's "address," the part of a city in which one lives. The industrial section, the

²*Social Class in America: The Evaluation of Status* (New York: Harper Torchbook, 1960), p. 7.

racial ghettoes, the exclusive subdivision, the trailer park, the commercial district—all these connote different kinds of status on the part of those who live there.

6. *Kinds of Furnishings and Equipment.*—The way in which people decorate their homes reflects something of their social status. The professional person may have many books and encyclopedias in his home with attractive book cases. The upper class family may have the same, but the furnishings are more likely to be antiques and heirlooms. Also, the middle class person may demonstrate his new status by the gadgets in his home, etc.

When one looks at these criteria carefully, he can see that although people take these symbols seriously, they only observe and do not discuss them. Ours is a competitive and comparative society. Adults "grade" themselves competitively along these six lines.

Social anthropologists have worked out ways of measuring social class according to these and other identifying characteristics. In doing so, they have identified six different social classes. These are arrived at by dividing each of the upper, middle, and lower classes into two groups, an upper and a lower. From this vantage point, we can approximate the following scheme of classes and the proportion of the population in each class:

Class	Percent	Description
Upper-Upper	2	The families of seniority and heritage, those with tradition
Lower-Upper	2	The "newly rich," new families of "self-made" folks who have been very successful but lack "background"
Upper-Middle	10	Well-to-do, well-educated, community-minded professional classes with some wealth

Lower-Middle	28	Respectable people of great dependability but not much wealth or means
Upper-Lower	33	Skilled workers, poor but honest and the salt of the earth type
Lower-Lower	25	The unskilled laborer, the day laborer, the uneducated, the ignorant, and shiftless

This background information gives context for discussing the drinking habits of the different social classes, the ways in which the high degree of movement of Americans from one class to another both inhibits and increases the extent and nature of drinking, and ways in which estrangement within this system may well be one of the contributing factors in producing both assuagement and retaliation drinking among Americans. Out of these kinds of drinking comes much that we know as alcoholism and other kinds of addictions.

Class Differences in Drinking Behavior

John Dollard, a social anthropologist who has done much research on caste and class, particularly in the southern regions of the United States, was one of the first to give expert opinion on the drinking habits found in the six social classes just described. For study purposes, I am quoting in full his description of these differences. This is a long quotation and careful study of it is necessary for the appreciation of this whole problem:

What is most evident about drinking behavior in these various class groups is that it differs a good bit. This is very important to notice. If we want to focus an educational program, we have to know where to focus it. Most Lower-Middle people are firmly opposed to indulgence in drinking, but this is not the case with Lower-Uppers.

In the Upper classes, drinking is not a moral issue. People at the top of our social structure drink a good deal; both sexes drink. Men and women drink in the same groups, in party style. There are, however, certain stiff controls here which do not exist in some of the lower classes. One is condemned in the Upper classes, not for drinking, nor for drunkenness, but for antisocial behavior while drunk. Fighting is taboo; aggressive behavior is heavily penalized even when expressed only in verbal assaults.

It is crucial to recognize the attitude of the Upper classes toward drinking because behavior patterns tend to sift downward in our society. Middle groups are likely to become tolerant and, perhaps, ultimately imitative of the customs of the topmost groups into which they, as individuals, would like to move. It might be said that the failure of Prohibition legislation lay in our social class system, for the highest people socially did not taboo drinking and their social customs were stronger than legislative controls.

In the Lower-Upper class we have the "cocktail set" who drink a good bit more recklessly than the people in the old families in the Upper-Upper class. The new families of wealth are in a rather insecure, frustrating position. They are constantly comparing themselves with the families who socially "own" the territory in which they live. The wealthy newcomers want to have an old homestead of their own; they want to have the prestige of lineage. Realizing that their great-grandfather was "just a butcher," rather than a powerful landowner, they suffer from a helpless feeling of inadequacy. Parental controls are weak and the scars from social competition painful, so Lower-Upper young people may try to escape from their social discomforts by drunkenness. There are case studies in several towns which lead us to suppose that there is some excessive, destructive drinking in this particular class group.

In the Upper-Middle class we have a strong evaluation of wealth and talent, and, ordinarily, moral values have restraint. However, the apparent nearness to the Upper classes and partial identification with this group have some effect on the drinking habits in the Upper-Middle class. In general, the men drink on social occasions, at their poker games and at casual gatherings in friends' houses, but Upper-Middle class women rarely drink. Drinking is not customary in mixed groups. Evidently, Upper-Middles have a neutral attitude toward drinking.

In the Lower-Middle class we would expect to find, with both sexes, a very strong taboo on drinking. Lower-Middle people value highly the traits of respectability which differentiate them from the Lower group. They emphasize this by rejecting the customs found in Lower classes. (Negroes in the Middle classes, for instance, will reject the spirituals and songs characteristic of Lower-class churches.

In this way they emphasize their difference in the social scale from the Lower-class individuals of their own race.) Lower-Middle men and women are the most stringent in exerting social control over drinking.

In the Upper-Lower class, which is the chief labor group, there is much more drinking. The Upper-Lowers do not have the same taboos as the Lower-Middles, but they do have some occupational restraints. A railway workman, for example, will tend to have an occupational taboo on drinking in some situations. In general, the Upper-Lowers drink at home and in the taverns, which provide a kind of club for Lower-class people. But if they are to be mobile into Lower-Middle class they have to change such habits.

Lower-class persons usually become openly aggressive when drinking because they have not been trained to exercise the control of aggression that is demanded of those at the top. In the Lower class, it is not a disgrace to get drunk and fight even if this behavior has dangerous consequences. A Lower-class man may be aggressive in the family toward wife and children. This group does not have the "drink like a gentleman" taboo. Differences in ethnic backgrounds are also conspicuous in the drinking customs of the Upper-Lower class—Irish, Jewish and Italian immigrants, for instance, retain customs that still have a "home color" when they settle in this country. There are differences as to beverages and controls of behavior. In the City of New Haven there are about 40,000 Italians; they drink wine with their meals. Some other ethnic groups, including the Jewish, have apparently a rather strong internal taboo on excessive drinking.

In the Lower-Lower class, drinking is socially unrestrained. There is the Saturday-night-to-Monday-morning binge, without much social control. Both men and women drink, although usually not in mixed groups. In the Lower-Lower class there is overt aggression; people are arrested for drunkenness, breaking the peace. There is much chronic drunkenness in this class.

None of these class controls is rigid. Of course, there are cross-class factors which tend to make some people drinkers in spite of their Lower-Middle taboos. Then they begin to move out of the Lower-Middle class, and the most tragic case is that in which the movement is downward.

The delineation of class lines in this discussion may seem too sharply marked. We are immediately reminded of the American dream of change of place through economic success, social usefulness and individual talent. Such mobility is not fiction; it is a fact, more so here than anywhere else. But we must remember that social mobility does not mean moving from $35 to $45 a week, or even to $200 a week. We can have Al Capone moving up in wealth but remaining a Lower-class Italian man. We cannot change our social skins very fast. Nevertheless, a man may change his social habits and ideals. These include standards of morality, propriety, clothes, recreation, liking for salads or for liquor, or the number of baths to be taken— all these are critical details of behavior.

If you are going to change your social level you will have to change your social habits, and this may mean your drinking habits. If you move from Middle to Upper, you will have to learn to drink. You may think this would be very simple, but social anthropologists have watched carefully nurtured Upper-Middle-class people moving into the Lower-Upper class who found it extremely difficult to learn the expected drinking habits. A lady who has been an eminently respectable person for 45 years and whose husband, for business considerations, moves in the Upper-class group, is expected to drink freely but finds it next to impossible. The Upper-class associates consider her a "dud," she spoils the party, and she gets pushed out. If she wishes to have her children know these people she will have to make a pretense, at least, of social drinking. You should not underestimate the difficulty in learning to drink if you are not used to it.

No doubt you are much more clear about and more impressed with the difficulty in learning *not* to drink; this familiar problem has been given a good deal of study. But if the Upper-Middle person moves up to the Lower-Upper group he has to change his habits in the direction of more alcoholic indulgence. If the custom of such indulgence is to be decreased, effort will have to be made to move more people into the Middle-class group and get more and more people to understand and accept the relative stringency of attitude of this group.

The task of changing social habits is no small undertaking. Such change cannot be accomplished by force alone, or law alone, because the sanctions which make people feel comfortable in the habits exist in their own social groups, and they do not care what outside groups think about them. Their habits have been built up and rewarded in the course of a long personal development, so changing some of these habits would be fairly difficult and slow. No one should feel badly who has tried to accomplish social changes swiftly and has failed.[3]

[3]*Alcohol, Science, and Society* (New Haven: Quarterly Journal of Studies on Alcohol, 1945), pp. 99-101.

On the basis of the various characteristics of social class which have been named above, one can take the following table prepared by Harold A. Mulford and get an overall statistical sampling of the United States population in terms of its drinking behavior. This is a national opinion research study of a sampling of 1,515 respondents who were selected by modified random sampling procedures to get an idea of the drinking practices of the noninstitutional population twenty-one years of age and over.

Two hundred interviewers using a structured questionnaire conducted the field work of this study in the summer of 1963, relating their findings to the work of Riley and Marden, who did a similar study in 1946.

The total number of those studied in the 1963 survey is in the first column, the percentage who drink is in the second column, the percentage who have previously drunk but have quit drinking is in the third column. The first three columns cover the entire sample. The second three columns cover a study of the drinkers only. The fourth column, therefore, represents the number of drinkers; the fifth column represents the quantity and frequency of drinking. This means that "type five" or heavy drinkers who drink medium or large quantities more than once a month are set forth in percentages of drinkers in the fifth column. The sixth column refers to the percentage of people who have had real trouble in drinking. These troubles are as follows: being fired or threatened to be fired if one does not quit drinking; being left or threatened to be left by one's spouse if one does not do something about his drinking; being charged by a family member of overspending on alcoholic beverages; being arrested for intoxication or other charges which involve the use of alcohol as a beverage; being told by a physician that drinking is injurious to the health of the subject.

With this explanation the following statistical study of regionalistic drinking patterns should be exceptionally illuminating.

Distribution of the Adult Population and of Selected Social Segments by Certain Measures of Drinking Behavior, U.S.A. 1963

	(1)	(2)	(3)	(4)	(5)	(6)
	ENTIRE SAMPLE			DRINKERS ONLY		
	N	*% Drink*	*% Quit(a)*	*N*	*% Q-F 5*	*% Troubles(b)*
Totals	1509	71	8	1068	11	10
Regions (c)						
New England	85	81	2	69	12	6
Mid Atlantic	283	88	4	249	12	8
E. N. Central	292	75	6	220	15	12
W. N. Central	139	74	6	103	9	4
S. Atlantic	196	64	10	126	6	11
E. S. Central	86	33	17	28	7	11
W. S. Central	182	48	9	87	7	13
Mountain	31	55	26	17	0	12
Pacific	215	79	9	169	9	11
Sex						
Male	737	79	9	580	16	16
Female	772	63	7	488	4	2
Age, Years						
21-39	641	79	4	505	10	10
40-59	551	70	9	386	12	10
60 and over	308	56	12	171	9	8
Education, Years (d)						
0-7	182	46	17	83	7	16
8	197	60	13	118	10	11
9-11	298	70	9	208	13	11
12	433	79	5	340	10	9
13-15	229	76	4	175	6	9
16	95	89	3	85	15	4
More than 16	71	79	3	56	21	13
Residence Community Size						
Under 2,500	261	60	8	157	5	6
2,500–9,999	293	69	9	201	12	8
10,000–74,999	427	76	7	323	11	8
75,000–499,999	278	71	7	198	10	13
500,000 and over	250	76	8	189	13	13

	(1)	(2)	(3)	(4)	(5)	(6)
	ENTIRE SAMPLE			DRINKERS ONLY		
	N	*% Drink*	*% Quit(a)*	*N*	% *Q-F 5*	% *Troubles(b)*
Religion						
Jewish	50	90	2	45	7	7
Catholic	378	89	5	336	12	10
Lutheran	136	85	4	116	13	5
Other large Prot. den *(e)*	156	81	6	127	12	6
Protestant den. unsp. *(f)*	46	78	9	36	17	14
Other non-Prot. religions	46	76	7	35	14	9
Methodists	218	61	8	133	5	8
Small Prot. denominations	191	53	14	102	10	15
Baptists	289	48	11	138	9	16
Income, Annual						
Under $3,000	279	54	14	151	8	7
3,000-4,999	307	64	5	195	5	12
$5,000-6,999	349	68	9	236	11	9
$7,000-9,999	290	85	3	247	12	10
$10,000 and over	237	87	4	207	14	9
Marital Status						
Single	121	79	2	95	18	16
Married	1211	72	8	871	10	9
Divorced	62	69	8	43	9	19
Widowed	113	51	12	58	5	2
Occupation (g)						
00-09	99	69	11	68	10	16
10-19	270	67	12	182	11	15
20-29	109	76	8	83	19	19
30-39	101	73	9	74	11	12
40-49	139	83	5	115	13	9
50-59	76	76	4	58	12	7
60-69	106	84	6	89	15	6
70-79	76	80	3	61	11	5
80-89	47	87	9	41	24	17
90-99	5	100	0	5	0	20

(a) Abstainers now who drank formerly.

(b) Had one or more "troubles" (see text) because of drinking.

(c) The states comprising each region are as follows: *New England:* Connecticut, Maine, Massachusetts, New Hampshire, Rhode Island, Vermont. *Middle Atlantic:* New Jersey, New York, Pennsylvania. *East North Central:* Indiana, Illinois, Michigan, Ohio, Wisconsin. *West North Central:* Iowa, Kansas, Minnesota, Missouri, Nebraska, North Dakota, South Dakota. *South Atlantic:* Delaware, Florida, Georgia, Maryland, North Carolina, South Carolina, Virginia, West Virginia, District of Columbia. *East South Central:* Alabama, Mississippi, Kentucky, Tennessee. *West South Central:* Arkansas, Louisiana, Oklahoma, Texas. *Mountain:* Arizona, Colorado, Idaho, Nevada, New Mexico, Utah, Wyoming. *Pacific:* Alaska, California, Hawaii, Oregon, Washington.

(d) Completions: 8 years=grade school, 12 years=high school, 16 years=college.

(e) "Other large Protestant denominations" includes Congregationalists, Presbyterians and Episcopalians. The prevalence rates in these three denominations varied little, ranging from 79 to 86%, but these rates were based on N's ranging from 29 Congregationalists to 82 Presbyterians.

(f) Protestants of unspecified denomination.

(g) This occupational classification is based on work originally done by the National Opinion Research Center (11) and attempts to arrange occupation according to socio-economic status. Much of the original work was done by P. K. Hatt and C. C. North. More recent work by O. D. Duncan can be found in Reiss (12, *especially ch. 6 and 7*). It is important to note that "housewives" are omitted, hence the rates of drinkers, etc., by occupation are not computed on the same base as is used for all other social segments. The following occupations illustrate the types in each category: 00-09, laborers, private household workers, janitors; 10-19, farmers, carpenters, painters; 20-29, shipping clerks, cabinet makers, mechanics; 30-39, machinists, salesmen, small business proprietors and managers; 40-49, electricians, construction foremen, nurses; 50-59, musicians, bookkeepers, manufacturing foremen; 60-69, real estate and insurance agents, secretaries, draftsmen; 70-79, buyers and store department heads, veterinarians, designers; 80-89, college professors, scientists, engineers; 90-99, dentists, lawyers, judges, physicians.[4]

By way of summary, one notes that quantity and frequency of drinking is higher in urban industrialized areas, but the amount of trouble the deviant drinker gets into is higher in the rural and smaller community areas of the country. Men are beset by the troubles associated with deviant drinking on the ratio of eight to one. People in the upper educational echelons have the highest percentage of deviant drinkers, and come out second only to those without any education in the amount of trouble that it causes them and their community.

From the point of view of religion, Methodists, Jews, and Baptists are lowest in their percentage of deviant drinkers, but Baptists are highest in the amount of trouble into which the deviant drinking gets them. However, whereas Jews have the

[4]Mulford, *op. cit.*, pp. 640-41.

highest rate of drinkers of any religion, they are next to the lowest in the rate of heavy drinkers. This leads Harold A. Mulford to hypothesize that whether an individual's drinking leads to trouble depends as much upon the community surrounding him as it does upon his own actions.

In short, it is impossible to understand and cope with the hydra-headed problems of the alcoholic either by "letting him off the hook" and treating him as an irresponsible child or by making him a moral whipping boy who is totally responsible for all that he does apart from the impact of the people around him. He is indeed a man of multiple troubles surrounded by a people of multiple troubles.

The Gottlieb Study

Another interesting study of social class and drinking habits was made by Gottlieb. In 108 interviews with bartenders and patrons of twenty-four taverns and twenty-two cocktail lounges in the Chicago area, he discovered some sobering information about the way in which the tavern or the cocktail lounge becomes a sort of "community." A cocktail lounge in this study was located in the commercial areas of Chicago. The taverns were located in residential areas in different parts of the suburban and interurban community. Gottlieb classified the people whom he interviewed according to the social status characteristics set forth by Lloyd Warner. He discovered that of the twenty-seven Upper-Middle-class people whom he interviewed in cocktail lounges, 96 percent of them spent from four to seven hours a week in a cocktail lounge drinking. Of fifty-four Lower-Middle-class persons, 72 percent spent from seven to twelve hours a week in a tavern drinking, talking, and socializing. Of fourteen persons in the Upper-Lower class, however, all of them spent twenty-three hours per week in a tavern. This might cause one to ask whether or not this time spent in the tavern is not a secularization of their need for a club or church.

The taverns were frequented in the morning and early afternoon by older persons, pensioners. They, and those younger persons who came later in the day, revealed similar socioeconomic and religious backgrounds, a sense of participation with others, and the rewarding feeling of belonging to a continuing group.

However, those who frequented the cocktail lounges were transients and not a cohesive group. The lounge provided a "bump-into-contact" opportunity for strangers to meet strangers.

On the basis of these data, one could ask what the church is doing in the inner-city to provide creative opportunities for strangers to have meaningful fellowship one with another in appropriate circumstance. Furthermore, one could ask what these communities of conviviality offer in the way of fellowship that can be legitimately met by the church rather than the tavern.[5]

David Pittman interviewed 187 men who had criminal careers as chronic police cases for alcoholism. From a social class point of view, only 3 percent of these people (compared with 22 percent in the general population) were professional people of the Upper-Middle class. Twenty-two percent of them (compared with 46 percent in the general population) were skilled workers. Unskilled laborers however, provided 68 percent of them (contrasted with 13 percent of them in the general population).[6] *

Whereas police case treatment is a common method of treatment, it is not the only one. Other methods of treatment are also associated with social class.

Treatment of Alcoholism and Social Class

Mentioning the police handling of chronic alcoholics brings up the whole problem of the varieties of treatment of alcoholics in

---

[5]D. Gottlieb, "The Neighborhood Tavern and the Cocktail Lounge," *The American Journal of Sociology,* LXII (n.d.), 559-62.

[6]"Criminal Careers of the Chronic Police Case Inebriate," *Quarterly Journal of Studies on Alcohol,* II (June, 1958), 255-68.

*In an upwardly mobile society such as the U.S.'s, different research techniques used at different times tend to produce different results (cf. earlier charts in the chapter).

different social classes. Social class affects the timing and the kind of treatment an alcoholic gets.

Religious association as prevention and treatment.—If we look upon religious groups as one form of social organization and association, we can observe that religious groups who have the lowest incidence of alcoholism, such as Jews, Methodists, and Baptists, nevertheless tend to be the harshest in the treatment of the alcoholic.

Furthermore, we notice that the quantity and frequency of drinking go up perceptibly as the preciseness, clarity, and depth of orthodox belief in religion lessens. For example, Charles Snyder found in a study of Jews that there is a "notable sobriety of Jews which is intrinsically connected with orthodox religious life." The following table of percentages shows how the quantity and frequency of getting drunk or "tight" increases as orthodoxy lessens.

	Drunk twice or more	*"Tight" more than 5 times*
Orthodox	9%	11%
Conservative	14%	14%
Reform	31%	38%
Secular	38%	41%

However, an additional social class factor enters into the above lessening of sobriety with the lessening of orthodoxy. When the same group of Jews were in lower income brackets, the above statistics remained relatively constant. But when they were in the higher income bracket, there was a perceptible upward swing in the amount of drunkenness. The Jews who got drunk twice or more in the lower income group and the higher income group were as follows:

	Lower income group	*Higher income group*
Orthodox	4%	18%
Conservative	14%	26%
Reform	24%	42%
Secular	38%	53%

But, Snyder says, "Such differences as exist in sobriety and intoxication between lower and higher income classes are related to the lower vitality of religious orthodoxy among higher classes."[7]

One has a hunch that the cohesiveness of the spiritual community as symbolized in the clarity and focus of beliefs is in itself a deterrent to alcoholism. However, this cohesiveness seems to disintegrate along with the theological orthodoxy as the group moves up the social ladder. Persons in the higher social classes have more competing organizations and a more fragmented affiliation system than do people in the lower classes. In other words, the church tends to be the one social and spiritual group outside the home to which people in the lower classes belong—those who do not frequent the taverns—whereas, in the upper classes the church is one among many competing loyalties from an organizational and associational point of view. Whither goes the fellowship and hither come the addictions!

Medical and institutional treatment.—Someone has said that a person in the upper classes is thought of as an "alcoholic" and a person in the lower classes is thought of as a "drunk" or a "bum." This wry humor reflects a half-consciousness of social class differentiation in the treatment of alcoholics. However, some more specific and careful studies of this have been made.

E. Gartly Jaco made a study of the incidence of mental disorders in the state of Texas under the auspices of the Russell Sage Foundation. Those persons in managerial, official, and proprietary occupations were generally the lowest in all kinds of mental disorders. However, in alcoholic or "toxic" disorders, managerial, official, and proprietary occupations of the upper classes were highest. Also, as has been pointed out before, the adjusted rate of disorders among the mentally ill in Texas revealed an extremely high correlation between alcoholism and drug addiction on the one hand and education on the other.

---

[7] "A Study of Drinking Patterns and Socio-Cultural Factors Related to Sobriety Among Jews," *Quarterly Journal of Studies on Alcohol,* XVI (1955), 505-32.

Education seems to be the most significant factor in moving people out of one social class into another. In Texas the adjusted rate of alcoholism and drug addiction was found to be highest among those who attended college.

Although the rate or incidence of alcoholism is higher among the educated and upper classes, the source of the first treatment of alcoholics shows a vivid disparity between social classes. A. B. Hollingshead and Fredrick C. Redlich, in a study of social class and mental illness, pointed out that 67 percent of the alcoholics in the first two upper social classes received their first treatment for alcoholism in private hospitals and with private practitioners. In the third class from the top, 83 percent of the alcoholics were treated first in private hospitals. In the bottom social class, 65 percent of the alcoholics were treated first in state hospitals, not in private hospitals.

As to type of therapy, the upper classes move toward and get individual psychotherapy, but only one third of the lower classes gets individual psychotherapy. Individual psychotherapy tends to be one of the prerogatives of the well-to-do from which the lower classes are excluded. Custodial care in alcoholism and other types of mental disorders tends to be the major therapy for people in the lower classes.[8]

Alcoholics of some social prestige in the community receive different treatment from those of lower classes. David Pittman's study of chronic police cases of alcoholics revealed that of 187 men studied, 68 percent of them were unskilled laborers and 3 percent of them were professional, whereas 22 percent of them were skilled workers. This suggests that strings might have been pulled in order to get persons in influential positions out of trouble with the law. Such influence is not available in many instances to the unskilled and skilled workers of the lower classes.

---

[8]*Social Class and Mental Illness* (New York: John Wiley and Sons, 1958), pp. 280-81, 289-90.

Some Guesses About Alcoholism, the Church, and Social Class

It is time for us to put some of the rich materials reviewed into some meaningful pattern of "hunches" as to what all this means for the church. In Alan Paton's novel *Cry the Beloved Country* a brokenhearted pastor, grieving over the plight of his people, says of the pastors and chieftains of South Africa: "The counselors of South Africa have counseled for everything except the matter of a broken community." In our attempt to counsel with alcoholics and their families, we are likely to have final answers for everything except the fact that the spiritual community of trust and love is shattered and filled with competition, distrust, and isolation.

We ought to observe first that, throughout the research we have reviewed, two outstanding motifs recur: First, as people move up the social ladder, their sense of community solidarity with one another is broken, isolation ensues, hostility and suspicion increase, and the drinking of alcohol becomes both a means of assuaging loneliness and retaliating for rejection imposed by the community; second, the religious community weakens both in its strength of belief and in its simplicity of institutional structure. As people move up the social ladder, they also tend to move from one denomination to another. They tend to diversify and pluralize their beliefs and group associations. As a result, they belong to many different organizations and are deeply related to none. Sensitivity to the effects of this movement must be a part of any full-orbed understanding of the problems of drinking in American life today.

A second observation points to the pathos of the middle classes. In more than name, the middle classes are caught in the middle. On the one hand, they have the need for stability and respectability which keeps them from slipping back into the old ways of the lower classes. As a result, they tend to be hard, rigid, and exclusivistic in their attitudes toward deviant behavior of any kind. Consequently, the middle classes tend to be more secretive about their indiscretions, lapses, and addictions. Therefore, the

major problem that the pastor of a middle-class church has in
dealing with alcoholism is to bring it out of hiding. Often the
process of addiction is far advanced before the church and its
ministry become even remotely aware of it. When this happens,
the need for stability and respectability creates such defensive-
ness and harshness of judgment that the church and its ministry
are further alienated from access to the person in the clutches of
alcohol. This is a very high price to pay for respectability. It
may well be the cause for the low incidence of drinking and
the high incidence of alcoholism and troubled people in the
churches that represent tthe middle classes most heavily—
Methodists and Baptists.

A third hunch or hypothesis concerning social class, the church,
and alcoholism is the contrary effect of the virtues of ambition,
industry, and frugality. These virtues are necessary for moving
out of a lower social class into an upper social class. Hard work
and ambition combined with frugality produce more goods, more
advantages, and more luxury. The "surpluses of society" are more
of a problem to the people in the upper classes than to those in
the lower classes. The spiritual issue of the well-to-do society
is that of handling its surpluses innocently and in such a way
as to adorn and not to deface human life. The anxiety of the
well-to-do who belong to a community in which they are not
comfortable makes facilitation drinking among them very common. Especially is this true of the "newly rich."

The pastor can be harsh and insensitive to the inner gnawing
of anxiety among the well-to-do. The pastor sees the drink
rather than feels the stress of the drinker, and in the process,
he overlooks the emptiness which the drinker is trying to fill.
This is the crucial issue involved in social drinking. This is the
danger involved when we as religious people inflict punitive
attitudes upon people who drink. In so doing we fall prey to
the legalism of which Paul spoke when he said that sin working
through the law beguiles the mind and makes sin all the more
sinful.

Finally, beneath these hypotheses or hunches resides the profound challenge of the Christian community at the point of social class: How can the church enable young people, especially young families, to move up out of the bare existence of the lower classes into some of the advantages of the upper classes without losing touch with themselves and without becoming secretive and covert about their social behavior in the new social groups of which they become a part? Second, how can the church develop a ruddy sense of stewardship that will capture the surpluses of the well-to-do and tie them to a broader and richer conception of stewardship than merely the support of an ecclesiastical organization? *The issues are fellowship at all levels of society and stewardship at its highest levels.*

Someone has said that all of the wounds of society are festering sores in the life of the alcoholic. The Lord Jesus Christ tells that inasmuch as we have seen or heard of these, we have seen or heard him. They are persons for whom he died. The more we understand ourselves and the more we understand the nature and message of the Lord Jesus Christ, the better we will understand the alcoholic.

IV

Alcohol, Parents, and Children

Between birth and death, nearly every individual has two families: the family into which he or she was born and the family which he or she establishes through marriage. Sociologists have called the first family the "family of orientation." Here is where everyone is introduced or "oriented" to life. Here, basic patterns for handling stress and gaining satisfaction in living are established. Habits are formed, and values are demonstrated by the parent and responded to by the child. The sociologists have called the second family the "family of procreation." Here is where everyone tests the patterns and habits of thought and action learned in the first family on the proving ground of a family of his or her own where he or she is the father or mother. Here children are born, making this the "family of procreation."

In the present chapter and the one succeeding, alcohol and alcoholism will be discussed in terms of the development of personality. The values of the Christian family will be the main concern of the discussion. In this chapter the role of alcohol and alcoholism in the "family of orientation" will be focused upon personality development in the formation of personality before marriage and parenthood. In the next chapter, the same approach will be taken to the development of personality in the adult after marriage and the establishment of his or her own home.

The Importance of Childhood Security

When the pathology of either the acute or the chronic alcoholic is "read backwards" into his developmental history, infantile tensions are discovered which still appear in him as an adult. As one wife said of her husband who is an alcoholic: "Why I have to tuck him in like a little baby after he has hit the bottle too hard!" She intuitively discerned his infantile need for a bottle. If you will observe very young children, their mouths are the center of their sensitivity. They will put their thumbs into their mouths, or their whole fists, or a piece of bread, a stick, or anything in sight. This satisfaction is what has been called by psychoanalysts "oral gratification." These actions relieve tensions and insecurity. In the alcoholic these oral activities continue. In other adults, eating sweets and foods of all kinds relieves anxiety and insecurity. The earlier psychoanalysts interpreted these problems quite biologically and traced overeating, overdrinking, and oversmoking to oral deprivation of the child in his earliest years.

Biological tensions are one dimension of the denials that little children have to bear. Those tensions represent much more important deprivations of love and security in their relationships to their mothers and fathers, particularly their mothers. The absence of mothers from children in the first three years of their lives as mothers go out of the home to work is a widespread practice. As children grow older, they need less mothering; but the younger they are, the more the denial of genuine mothering devastates them. They grow up with an insatiable craving for dependence. Similarly, the mother and/or father who limit an older child's self-reliance by doing his playing, thinking, deciding, and choosing for him perpetuate and increase the habit of dependence.

Later psychotherapists, such as the contemporary Erik Erikson, interpret the personal security and need for dependency of the infant and child in terms of learning "basic trust." The child requires a *trustworthy* parental relationship for real emotional security. The word "confidence" could be used, but trust implies a certain childlikeness and mutuality. When the child has fears of being left, of being left empty, of being starved for stimulation, he can very early feel himself to be of little worth. Erikson says that "the establishment of a basic sense of trust in earliest childhood makes adult individuals less dependent upon mild or malignant forms of addiction, on self-delusion, and on avaricious appropriation."[1]

When we put this into a Christian context, remarkedly enough Erikson says: "Whosoever says he has religion must derive a faith from it which is transmitted to infants in the form of basic trust; Whosoever claims that he does not need religion must derive such basic faith from elsewhere."[2] Yet, the very absence of this kind of security-providing element of trust appears vividly in the alcoholic personality. For example, Howard Jones made a study of seventy-two alcoholics in Toronto, Canada. Half of them were inmates of a prison. The other half were being treated for alcoholism in a public clinic. Over half of these men showed exceptionally dependent attitudes towards their mothers, and nearly half of them revealed similarly dependent attitudes toward their wives. When the wife of a given inmate had not been willing to cooperate with the dependency-situation demands of the alcoholic, it had led to severe marital conflict as a part of the drinking problem. Where the wife cooperated with the dependency, marital conflict was lowered, but the alcoholism became more chronic.[3] In these instances, drink was a way of compensating for the absence of the mother, not because the mother was responsible for his drinking, but because drinking made the alcoholic feel childlike and dependent again. It is as if alcoholism retaliates upon the whole world as the alcoholic feels himself becoming a burden on society.

---

[1] *Identity and the Life Cycle* (New York: International Universities Press, 1959), p. 63.

[2] *Ibid.*, p. 65.

[3] *Alcoholic Addiction* (London: Tavistock, 1963), pp. 50-51.

In the Christian community of the church, the pastor and deacon meet regularly the situation in which a sentimental, very religious, but sweetly domineering woman is the mother of a "wayward son" who drinks too much. Sisters and wives fit into the drama of overprotection as well. Other persons—pastors, schoolteachers, law enforcement officers, and public officials—are often "used" by the mother to continue the indulgence of the black sheep of the family. These mothers are not to be dealt with harshly or without understanding, but, as Howard Jones says, the "real prophylaxis against alcoholism" needs to be directed against the causes themselves. Why are the mothers' needs for keeping their sons dependent so excessive? Could they be reduced, or is there some way that these needs could be met in a less destructive way? Often these mothers are given a hyphenated name by the community: "the-finest-Christian-woman-I've-ever-seen." This view equates the dependency-maintaining matriarchy with Christian virtue.

A clinical example of this is a thirty-year-old man, married, the father of two little girls, four and six years of age. He was in business with his father and lived in the home with his father and mother, both families under the same roof. The situation came to the pastor's attention because the man was terribly fearful of taking the Lord's Supper on communion day. The man's mother was a "teetotaler," an active leader in the church. She began her conversations with the pastor about her son's fear of taking communion. She could not understand this. Upon closer study of the problem with her, the pastor discovered the mother also to be anxious about her son's deviant drinking. She even associated his fear of taking communion with his anxiety over drinking anything that reminded him of alcohol. She used alcohol and abstinence as a means of maintaining extensive control over all the decision-making processes, not only of this son, but also of her husband and other four children. An older son was in an institution for the treatment of alcoholics. Religious activity of the family was kept up on an outward "pleasing-mother" basis until the mother died. Then the family gradually discontinued all relationship to any religious group. Only a little understanding of this was ever developed by either son or mother.

Social Insecurity in School-age Children

Although children should be somewhat self-reliant before they start to school, they still have to reckon with the problems of being away from home and of meeting strange people for the first time. In the years just prior to entering school, a healthy child learns to exercise initiative in his home life without having to feel guilty for having done so. He or she learns to walk, talk, run, climb, and to have a healthy governor of conscience on his or her newfound strengths. As Erikson says, the child only feels independent when he is thoroughly secure in the fundamental values he has learned. This internal dependence upon one's own personal sense of law and order Erikson calls conscience. Whereas basic trust is formed in the early years and is related to the institution of religion, conscience is formed in terms of the principle of adult authority *outside* as well as inside the home. With this inner security a child can move out of the home with a confident expectation that the authority of other adults, such as policemen and teachers, will allow him freedom which, if rightly used, will not lead to shame, embarrassment, and guilt. It is the kind of joy in relation to life expressed by a second-grade boy in a letter to a policeman who spoke to the class on safety and traffic rules. The child said: "Thanks for coming to our class. I liked you better than recess even."

Furthermore, a child learns to take his or her role in life as a member of his or her own sex. A little boy learns to be a little boy without fear or shame. Parents like and accept the child as he is without trying to change the order of God's creation. On the other hand, a child can have his self-confidence shaken by being deprived of the right to be himself. A father can have wanted a son so badly that he tries to make his daughter over into a son.

A mother can be so fearful of the opposite sex—particularly her husband—that she "sissifies" her son. When the alcoholic father comes into the home, brutalizes the mother and children, the children become fearful and confused. Little girls become fearful of men, and little boys doubt that they want to be men. At this point, although alcoholism is not hereditary, it can create so much insecurity in children that they are predisposed to use alcohol as a way of handling the insecurity. But more likely than this, they will become crusaders against drink.

The equipment the home gives the child in personal security becomes the means for developing socially secure relationships when the child starts to school. The child learns "how to get busy with something and how to be busy with others." He learns to make things. He develops a sense of industry which stands over against feelings of social inferiority. What a crisis in his emerging sense of interpersonal competence! Creativity is required of him! Can he produce? Here the teacher has much to do with the confidence and competence produced in the child. The child is very aware of the teacher's presence and of the presence of other children. He forms specific pictures of how he feels about himself as a participant in a structured social situation such as the schoolroom is. He may see himself as shy and unsure in his dealings with other people. He may see himself as confident and relatively sure of himself. This may be true of his estimate of himself in relation to his friends at school alone and not particularly in other respects. He may feel very confident of his reading ability, exceptionally proud of the house he lives in, sure of his mother's protection. But his self-image suffers when it comes to his ability to meet strangers, to participate in a social group, or to carry on a conversation. This may persist into adulthood as a pattern of life. Drinking may later be one of his ways of changing temporarily his image of himself. Social insecurity shapes the drinking habits of adults and is one factor in addictive drinking.

Howard Jones's depth study of seventy-two alcoholics reflects the importance of the problem of social insecurity in the life of adult alcoholics. Emotional deprivation was characteristic of twenty-four out of thirty cases identified as being socially insecure. Unlike the group suffering from parental overprotection, this group revealed a *lack* of important ingredients in an effective family development in relation to parents. The lack of a father in the home, the excessive absence of the father from the home, continued rejection by the mother in the home, or continuous conflict between mother and father were causes of this deprivation.

Parental Adequacy

Lee N. Robins, William M. Bates, and Patricia O'Neal did a Foundation Fund and U.S. Public Health Service study of adult drinking patterns of former problem children. They did a follow-up study of every child seen in the St. Louis Municipal Psychiatric Clinic in the years 1924 to 1929. They did this study thirty years later, from 1954 to 1959, after the clinic experience of the 524 patients, 503 of whom survived to the age of twenty-five. Using both the personal interview and the standardized questionnaire, they focused their research on the relationship of problems in the parent-child situation thirty years earlier to the alcoholism that appeared later.

One area they explored was that of *parental adequacy*. Parents were judged to be inadequate if for any reason—irresponsibility, antisocial behavior, physical or mental disease—they failed to function responsibly as parents. Neglect, desertion, excessive drinking, and flagrantly illegal acts were considered indications of parental inadequacy. They discovered that antisocial behavior of nonsupport, being arrested, cruelty, and desertion by the father ranked high and more frequently as a factor in the lives of the children who later became alcoholics than did the father's drinking itself. The father's drinking was evident in 38 percent of the pasts of those who were alcoholics later in life. The father's being arrested, however, was present in 70 percent, while desertion was present in 48 percent of the case studies.[4]

The world in which a male child has to become an adult is a man's world. Although the dependency problems of alcoholics point to a defective relationship to their mother, the problems of social inadequacy point toward defective relationships between the alcoholic and his father. Absentee fathers, deserting fathers, cruel fathers, and antisocial fathers are the kind named in careful research studies. Yet, one asks the question: "Why is it that one child in the home of such a father will become alcoholic and another will become a paragon of virtue, maybe even enter the ministry?" One answer is that the Christian community around the family provides effective substitutes for inadequate fathers in one child's case and not in the other. Another answer is that some children will respond with retaliatory drinking as they grow older. Other children will have a "reverse" response and react with a negative identity which, for the community's sake, turns out to be more socially acceptable than the antisocial behavior of the father.

On the other hand, alcoholism is just one of the many disorders of living that can happen to persons with similar backgrounds. Alcoholism was the "symptom of choice" from the Pandora's box of possibilities whereby these men filled the gap between the demands of their world and their feeling of competency to meet those demands. A chronic physical illness, a running battle with an associate, a fanatic fringe group with an authoritarian leader, an open psychotic break with reality—all these could have provided the compensation for feelings of "dis-ease" and discomfort in the presence of a demanding social situation.

If the emotional deprivations just described are deep enough and severe enough, the role of alcohol in facilitating an individual's social access to his community would imperceptibly, but certainly, career into assuagement drinking and retaliative

[4]*Society, Culture and Drinking Patterns,* David Pittman and Charles Snyder, eds. (New York: John Wiley, 1962), pp. 395-430.

drinking of a compulsive and uncontrolled order. This is the tricky course over which the social drinker runs, and may explain why some people drink socially all their lives and others gradually become hooked. For some people, eating excessively could mean, psychologically, the same thing. For others, getting and spending money could outdistance the real demands of life and become an end within itself, pursued compulsively and without control. But, as Reverend G. Allen West of Nashville has observed, "It should be kept in mind that alcohol is a drug and has habit-forming power, which food does not have necessarily."

Preadolescent Friendships

We often lump all adolescent children into one category. Careful distinctions need to be made in understanding adolescent persons at different stages of their lives between ages ten and twenty-two. It is even more important to see them in terms of the kinds of relationships which are most meaningful to them at a given time, rather than in terms of the chronological year in which they happen to be living. When we do this, we can define adolescence in terms of at least four different stages: (1) preadolescence, (2) early adolescence, (3) late adolescence, and (4) culturally-delayed adolescence by reason of increased educational demands for graduate and professional work. The development of drinking patterns and the roots of alcoholism can be seen more vividly by making these four distinctions than it can by lumping all adolescent persons into a vague subculture known as "teen-agers."

In preadolescence—somewhere between the ages of eight and one-half and twelve or thirteen—a spectacular interest in another person of one's own sex emerges. This other person becomes intensely important to him or her. Harry Stack Sullivan has given us the most enchanting and precise understanding of this need of a boy or a girl for a "chum." He says, "If you will look very closely at one of your children when he finally finds a chum . . . you will discover something very different in that relationship—

namely, that your child begins to develop a real sensitivity to what matters to another person." He becomes concerned and learns how to collaborate and cooperate with a person of his own age and sex.

This is not a sexual involvement but what Sullivan calls 'interpersonal intimacy" or responsible closeness. In this responsible closeness the young person normally learns how to formulate the adjustments of his own behavior in such a way as to appreciate and sense the needs of the other person in the pursuit of common concerns, common goals, and almost identical objectives. This is more than just cooperating. It is unselfish collaboration. The friends gallantly "supply each other with satisfactions and take on each other's successes in the maintenance of prestige, status, and all the things which represent freedom from anxiety or the diminution of anxiety."[5] Fritz Kunkel earlier called this the "emergence of the we." In the language of the New Testament, this is the "phileo" kind of love—that is, the love of friend for friend. It is the genuine concern of a young person for another young person's well-being.

The groundwork for trustful intimacy, so indispensable in the adult institutions of business organization, political life, educational pursuits, and church life especially is laid at this crucial time in young people's lives. Remarkably enough, this is the time when considerable numbers of young persons unite their lives with Jesus Christ in baptism and begin to participate in the fellowship of the church. The church provides a natural and wholesome opportunity, alongside that of the public school, for preadolescent boys to have responsible and close fellowship with a chum. Similarly, girls have excellent opportunities in the church to form "chumships." The adults who are working with them as Sunday School teachers, public school teachers, Scout leaders, and so forth, should be aware of how important a preadolescent boy or girl is to his or her chum. Camp experiences,

[5]*The Interpersonal Theory of Psychiatry* (New York: W. W. Norton, 1953), pp. 245-46.

summer assembly visits, and weekend retreats provide excellent opportunities for dependent young people to launch out into new experiences and, at the same time, not to have to do so alone.

Parents can contribute to the security and confidence of their own child by showing appreciation for and devotion to the interests and needs of their children's friends. When the family has to move abruptly, these relationships are disrupted. Parents who are sensitive should encourage correspondence and visits during these times of transition until new friendships can be formed.

Furthermore, parents, as well as pastors and teachers, should watch carefully the ways in which adults sometimes exploit preadolescent boys and girls. Immature and emotionally disturbed teachers and leaders can try to take the place of a pal in the life of the preadolescent. This simply will not work. An adult can be a friend and a trustworthy guide, but not a chum. Sticky sentimentalism wrongly interprets the needs of these fifth and sixth graders for a "chummy" relationship to adults. This may even become pathological in the exploitation of a child by a confirmed homosexual. The veteran and experienced pastor may be responsible for the pastoral care of such pathologically disturbed persons as homosexuals, but, at the same time, he is responsible for seeing to it that, as the apostle Paul says, "others are not taught to do these things."

Up to this point, I have described preadolescence in terms of its normative patterning in the "chumship" stage. The ideal is that these relationships of preadolescence be intense enough that the young person can get to know the other person in a genuinely intimate friendship without, at the same time, becoming fixated in such a way that it becomes an absorbing relationship.

The main thing that preadolescents learn from one another is that it is all right to be interested in the opposite sex and that from each other they can gain courage in learning to talk with people of the opposite sex and of their own age. Moving out of preadolescence into social relationships with the opposite sex is a demanding kind of growth. It demands courage and security. Having another young person his own age with whom to share both joyful and fearful experiences provides strength and courage. This helps equip him for later courtship.

Without this, loneliness reaches its full significance. Loneliness becomes that great inner emptiness which we have difficulty in describing or even remembering. This loneliness is the breeding ground, and preadolescence seems to me to be the spawning season, for the kind of inner craving which leads to alcoholism.

People who are afraid of close relationships to others need some form of "booster" to move them over the hump, and that becomes an habitual invention for facilitating the necessary closeness in individual and group relationships. Alcohol is one of these boosters. It is a tool of the security operation whereby the timid seem temporarily brave and the isolated seem momentarily sociable. I am not aware of any detailed research on the relationship of preadolescent loneliness to later alcoholism. I am convinced, on the basis of work with people plagued by many different kinds of compulsion, that both a sound doctrine of the Christian community and a health-giving relationship within the family call for the preventive attention of pastors and parents to this crucially important era in the lives of "Junior boys and Junior girls."

The Quest for Identity

We are accustomed to calling the early and late adolescent boy or girl "teen-agers." However, this tends to cut them loose from the adult community and to make a separate "subcommunity" of them. It is more accurate to call this group "emerging young adults."

They are not yet adults in every respect. Legally, they are thought of as minors. Yet they have many of the bodily and mental abilities of adults. They are neither children nor adults, but both at the same time. Hence, this creates conflict for them, both within and without. They do not want to be treated as children, but are insecure in the demands of being an adult. Both parent and pastor, public school teacher and Sunday School teacher, must come to terms with this double-edged dilemma of the emerging young adults whom we call teen-agers.

The major task of the early and late adolescent is coming to terms with who he is and making decisions as to what his place in life will be. The psychologists today call this the "search for identity." This search moves along three lines. First, the youth is searching for adequate leaders and is learning how to be a leader and follower in his group of fellow young persons. Second, the young person is defining his position in life by settling upon some basic beliefs about himself, others, and the world in which he lives. Third, the young person is coming to terms with himself or herself as a sexual person as over against and in relation to persons of the opposite sex.

As these three great searches go on, the young person is being pushed by family, school, and church to "achieve." It is little wonder that at times he feels they are actually "shoving" him, and he begins to rebel.

Early adolescence, roughly equivalent to the high school years, begins at the time the young person becomes genuinely interested in people of the opposite sex and continues until the time the sexual identity and behavior of the young person has taken on a definite pattern of responsible relationship to the opposite sex. This is a big transition. It is accompanied by other adventures, such as learning to drive an automobile, learning to stay away from home over longer periods of time without undue home-sickness, learning to handle money, and learning to make good decisions about one's friendships.

There is much trial-and-error learning by human example here. The particular kind of learning we are interested in in this book is learning to drink alcohol. What does the research say about drinking habits of teen-agers, particularly those in high school? Raymond McCarthy has done a careful study in an effort to answer this question. Up until his study, reliable information on the extent of high school students' drinking and their attitudes toward drinking practices was very scarce indeed. Usually, attitudes and opinions concerning the use of alcohol by this group are founded upon unusual, isolated, and highly publicized escapades that groups of teen-agers have. McCarthy and others, however, conducted such studies in different parts of the country. Analysis of their information reveals several things.

Most of the drinking was in the upper grades of high school. Most of the drinking was done with the consent of parents. In 1948 a Purdue opinion poll checked the attitudes of three thousand high school students in all parts of the country. Only 11 percent of them approved of drinking, 30 percent were neutral, and 55 percent were heartily disapproving. In actual practice 65 percent of them said that they did not drink and 35 percent said that they did drink. They reflected their approval and disapproval, their practice and refusal to drink as follows (listed by grade levels).

	9th	10th	11th	12th
Disapprove of drinking	65%	64%	57%	48%
Sometimes drink	28%	28%	37%	47%

In different parts of the country, the percentages appear as follows:

	East	Midwest	South	Mt.-Pacific
Disapprove of drinking	58%	57%	66%	50%
Sometimes drink	34%	41%	28%	38%[6]

In a 1955 study of drinking practices of high school students in Nova Scotia, questions were asked of pupils in grades nine to twelve. Drinking in situations for reasons of ritual or family custom, such as religious ceremonies, wedding feasts, family rituals, and so on, was excluded. Of 5,409 students, 1,636 drank occasionally, moderately, or frequently.

---

[6]*Teenagers and Alcohol* (New Haven: Yale Center of Alcohol Studies, 1956), p. 22.

The most outstanding fact about the drinking of high school students is that it begins in the home. Pastors and public school teachers responsible for guiding high school youth must recognize that students in every classroom come to the classroom from families who have widely varying attitudes toward alcohol usage. In school the young person hits cultural conflict head-on. The integrity of the things he has been taught at home is at stake whether he drinks or does not drink, whether he thinks one should drink or should not drink. Also, the young person may be the child of one or both parents who themselves are "problem drinkers," or alcoholics in the fullest sense of the word. Exceptional sensitivity is needed in relation to teen-agers whose parents are alcoholics.

Alcoholics Anonymous has organized a group called Alateen, which is a group of young people who seek help with problems that arise when alcoholism afflicts the parent or other close relatives or friends. The objective of Alateen is to teach the young person to detach himself emotionally from his parent's difficulties as much as possible, while continuing to love his parents. Alateen strives to enlighten teen-agers as to their own faults and failings which may or may not come from living with the alcoholic parent. Inspiration and spiritual undergirding aims to give any young person between twelve and twenty who is troubled by the alcoholic behavior of a relative or friend membership and support in an understanding group. This is exactly what a Sunday School class, a church, a Training Union can and often does mean to a young person whose parent is addicted to drinking.

High school drinking, as one high school boy put it, is more of an adventure that it is an effort. "They drink to be drinking and not to get drunk." Where high school young people do drink, it is usually a continuation of the behavior patterns they learn in the home, and not something they learn from "bad companions." In the public schools, the modern young high schooler has to learn to cope with a variety of standards concerning drinking, and the most important channel of guidance is open lines of communication between the parent and the child.

Erik Erikson calls the focusing of the identity of a young person in his belief, his relationship to authority persons, and his companionship with the opposite sex the formation of a strong sense of "I." These are "ego" structures built at the center of the person's being. The ego, from this point of view, is not "selfishness" in some moralistic sense, but something of a stackpole around which the total personality is built. It is like the spire of a cathedral pointing heavenward telling the world who this person is! This ego-identity calls for real separation from mother and father, brother and sister. In scriptural terms, this means that the person "leaves father and mother" and cleaves to his wife and the twain become one flesh.

In the case of alcoholics, a considerable number suffer from confused identity and a weak ego structure. This appears to be one root of alcoholism growing out of the teen years. Howard Jones in the Toronto studies found that out of the seventy-two cases he studied, seventeen of them fell into "the diagnostic category of ego-need, and, . . . there was unmistakable evidence of strong feelings of inferiority, either frankly admitted to the interviewer or displayed indirectly, but no less clearly, by the way in which the individual . . . met the vicissitudes of life."[7] These cases did not belong to clubs when they were children; in sports they were shy in joining teams; and as they grew older, even though they wanted to date girls, they seemed never to have the courage to ask.

A second root of alcoholism in the teen years is the amount of isolation many young people experience in relation to their parents when they begin to pass the parents in education. This is particularly true of young people who are born into the lower classes as the children of persons with less than a high school education. As these children move into senior high school, the

---

[7]Howard Jones, *op. cit.*, p. 93.

educational and social distances and the differences in value judgments begin to widen considerably unless the parents have been the kind of people who have gone to great extremes to become "self-educated," or unless the parents are the kind of people who learn from their children what their children learn at school. Thus, the very education for which many lower class persons are ambitious for their children to have becomes a gradually widening wedge, separating them from their children in many different ways.

Drinking is one of the habits that young people isolated from their parents take up as a symbol of their new sophistication and as a card of entry into a new social group. The church can do much for the parents of such young people because the church itself is an educational institution when it is at its best. Much informal education can be gotten to the parents at this point, and such structures as the informal programs of Sunday School and adult study groups can do much to help the parents keep abreast of the educational growth of their children. This cuts down the amount of loneliness and creates more fellowship between parent and child.

College Drinking

Ernest Groves used to say that the human being has a longer period of infancy than any other creature. It takes us longer to learn to feed ourselves, to walk, to communicate. Further, our culture demands of certain ones that they delay immediate decisions in order to prepare themselves for a profession. One would surmise, therefore, that this extra strain caused by the increased complexity of our society would pose greater possibilities of deviant drinking in those persons who go to college. If the percentage of drinkers and deviant drinkers goes up progressively with the amount of education, does this mean that the habit of drinking is learned in college?

Robert Straus and Seldon Bacon made an extensive study of college drinking habits. Their survey showed that 89 percent of college students came from homes in which both parents were drinkers, and that of those who came from homes where both parents abstained, 54 percent were themselves abstainers. Parental example is one of the most important factors in the decisions of college youth as to whether to drink. Also, parental disapproval of drinking has much more effect on students' behavior than negative preachments from either the church or the school.

When asked why they drank, college students interviewed in Straus and Bacon's study gave the following answers, set forth in a percentage table according to their reasons for drinking:

Per Cent of Male Students Ascribing Importance to Each of 12 Reasons for Drinking, by Type of Beverage Most Frequently Used

	Students Who Most Frequently Use		
Reason for Drinking	Beer	Wine	Spirits
	(per cent ascribing some or considerable importance to each reason)		
To get along better on dates	36	15	36
To relieve fatigue or tension	56	47	55
To be gay	66	41	63
To relieve illness or physical discomfort	26	26	28
To comply with custom	65	53	66
Because of enjoyment of taste	77	65	72
In order not to be shy	27	26	24
As an aid in meeting crises	8	12	12
For a sense of well-being	18	21	28
As an aid in forgetting disappointments	29	18	23
To get high	53	24	42
To get drunk	16	9	17[8]

As to quantity and frequency of drinking, Straus and Bacon concluded that the portion of students who drank frequently and heavily was very small. Those who drank extensively tended to use alcohol at its lowest limits in beer and with minimal

---

[8]*Drinking in College* (New Haven: Yale University Press, 1953), p. 91.

criteria for frequency and amount of drinking done. Only 14 percent of male students drank excessively. However, the whole problem of the extent of drinking must be considered qualitatively as well as quantitatively, and Straus and Bacon aptly point out that "the boy or girl who has never before touched alcoholic beverages, who on one occasion takes three drinks, and never again touches liquor may suffer more damage from this one experience than a boy or girl who ordinarily drinks this amount fifty times a year."[9]

One of the most surprising revelations of the study of drinking in college is the place at which college students reported having first learned to drink. We in religious professions are interested in the companions with whom college students do their first postchildhood drinking.

Straus and Bacon give the following information on early drinking traits:

Companions at First Postchildhood Drinking (in per cent)

	Students Who Drink	
Companions	Men	Women
Family	27	51
Close friends, same sex	53	11
Others, same sex	3	—*
Close friends, opposite sex or mixed group	13	32
Others, opposite sex or mixed group	2	5
Other (includes alone)	2	1
Total	100	100[10]

* <0.5%.

Furthermore, the following information concerning the usual place at which college persons drank is remarkably revealing in that college rooms and fraternity and sorority houses had the lowest frequency as places of drinking, whereas students more often drank in their own homes, at restaurants, taverns, and bars.

---

[9]*Ibid.*, p. 117.
[10]*Ibid.*, p. 122.

Usual Place of Drinking (in per cent)

Place	Men			Women		
	Beer	Wine	Spirits	Beer	Wine	Spirits
Own home	15	55	14	18	67	16
Home of a friend	9	19	18	13	15	14
College room	3	3	5	1	1	1
Fraternity or sorority house	3	1	3	6	—*	4
Restaurant, tavern, or bar	60	13	22	47	11	22
Night club	5	4	28	8	3	37
Private club	2	2	5	1	1	4
Other	3	3	5	6	2	2
Total	100	100	100	100	100	100[11]

*<0.5%.

The Straus-Bacon studies searched for potential problem drinkers among college students who drank. They found that about 6 percent of male student drinkers and 1 percent of women student drinkers showed signs of being potential problem drinkers. These problem drinkers had, to greater or lesser extent, experienced forewarning signs of problem drinking, namely having blackouts, becoming drunk alone, drinking before or instead of breakfast, and showing aggressive behavior while drinking. However, a significant finding was that these potential problem drinkers in college reflected exceptionally high anxiety about their behavior. Consequently, college students who are problem drinkers were demonstrated to be considerably more open to constructive counseling at this early stage than would be true of other drinkers. The health services of colleges and universities can therefore do much in the prevention of later alcoholism by locating, isolating, and bringing into treatment these problem drinkers.

Too much of the approach by colleges and universities to the problem drinker is based on a psychology of fear. Church-related colleges especially view with alarm and react defensively

---

[11]*Ibid.,* p. 124.

toward the student in trouble with drink. This apparently serves only to bury the problem or chase it off campus. A more creative approach would be a curricular and extracurricular program of alcohol education plus firm rules about the use of alcohol on campus.

Howard Clinebell has summarized the development of alcoholic symptoms as reported by E. M. Jellinek. The characteristic kinds of behavior are located at the ages at which they appeared in the drinking histories of the alcoholics. As a process, alcoholism started at 18.8 years of age and reached its lowest point at 40.7 years of age.

THE ADDICTIVE PATTERN

	Number Reporting (out of 98)	*Average or Mean Age* (of first occurrence)
Characteristic Alcoholic Behavior		
1. Getting drunk	98	18.8
2. Blackouts	89	25.2
3. Sneaking drinks	89	25.9
4. Week-end drunks	74	27.2
5. Loss of control	95	27.6
6. Extravagant behavior	77	27.6
7. Rationalization	81	29.2
8. Losing friends	63	29.7
9. Morning drinks	91	29.9
10. Indifference to quality (liquor)	84	30.0
11. Losing working time	90	30.4
12. Midweek drunks	78	30.4
13. Family disapproval	95	30.5
14. Losing advancements (on job)	56	30.6
15. Go on water wagon	80	30.7
16. Losing job	56	30.9
17. Daytime drunks	85	31.0
18. Solitary drinking	87	31.2
19. Antisocial behavior	60	31.3
20. Benders	89	31.8
21. Remorse	91	32.2

22. Protecting supply (of liquor)	77	32.5
23. Tremors	90	32.7
24. Changing drinking pattern	73	32.7
25. Fears	72	32.9
26. Resentment	69	33.1
27. Seeking psychiatric advice	53	35.0
28. Sedatives	60	35.5
29. Felt religious need	60	35.7
30. Seeking medical advice	80	35.8
31. Hospitalization	60	36.8
32. Admit to self inability to control	98	38.1
33. Admit to others inability to control	91	39.5
34. Reached lowest point (hit bottom)	97	40.7[12]

This whole chapter has been devoted to studying drinking habits and alcoholism in relation to several developmental phases of the life of people before marriage. The problems of dependency have been related to early infancy; the problems of social security have been related to childhood; problems of identity and ego-need have been related to early adolescence; and the effects of leaving and going to college have been related to drinking habits while in college in late adolescence.

The next chapter will take up the problems of drinking as they arise in the "family of procreation."

---

[12]*Understanding and Counseling the Alcoholic* (New York: Abingdon Press, 1956), pp. 25-26.

V

Alcohol and Marriage

Considerable evidence points to the fact that well over half of American families use alcohol in the home. This indicates a shift in drinking behavior since the turn of the century. Americans are moving toward the German pattern of drinking beer rather than hard liquor in the home, and are also first learning to drink in the home.

As more has been learned about alcohol and alcoholism, changes of attitude toward the alcoholic's family have been noted also, changes in the cultural evaluation of the relationship between alcoholic and spouse or children.

Joan Jackson traces these shifts. In the early years of the century, the alcoholic's family members—his wife and children ordinarily—were thought of as innocent victims. They were pitied, given charity, and the alcoholic himself "was seen as someone for the family to hide, the police to control, and the clergy to reform." He was treated as a bad boy who needed a spanking and a good lecture.

Then Americans moved into a second phase of their attitudes toward the alcoholic. Members of the alcoholic's family were no longer thought of as innocent victims, but as culprits in their own right. The wife was often dubbed as the kind of woman who would drive any man to drink. A sort of marketplace detective work was reflected in those community attitudes toward the alcoholic and his family. The amateur sleuth gathered evidence, fixed blame, prosecuted the case, and the rest of the community served as jury and judge. The unrealism of these two attitudes, both from the point of view of what has been learned about alcohol and its effects and from the point of view of a sound ethical perspective of the alcoholic and his family, is hard to overestimate.

Consequently, a third shift is now in the making in terms of Americans' attitudes toward alcoholics. This might be called an "interaction" attitude. This means that the alcoholic and his family interact with each other and serve as both cause and effect, impinging upon each other in a sort of reciprocity of responsibility. In this attitude, "blame fixing" recedes, and distribution of responsibility comes to the fore. The family is seen as a totality, and its members both as responsible people, on one hand, and victims on the other. The present attitude, especially among those who are trained in the understanding of alcoholism, springs out of the view that alcoholism is an illness.

The pastor, the deacon, and the members have to come realistically to grips with the simultaneous presence of all three of these attitudes in the church. The alcoholic and his family may be caught between several groups of people having differing attitudes, and the resulting moral and social confusion can be damaging in itself. The "interaction" view of the alcoholic and his family is the point of view set forth in this chapter; but hard-nosed commitment to the alcoholic and his family requires that we recognize this cultural confusion and the attitudes of average church members toward the alcoholic and his wife and children.

With this attitudinal exploration in mind, we are in a position now to appreciate the kinds of interaction and interpersonal problems that arise between the alcoholic and his "family of procreation," that is, the marriage partner and children. Let us look first at the factor of marital choice.

Mate Choice

We know several things about the relationship of marital choice and alcoholism. Casework shows clinically that the alcoholism of a mate is quite often known by the other partner before marriage. Particularly is this true in a certain kind of marriage. A considerable number of nurses, for example, who have strong "mothering needs" choose a known alcoholic for a husband. Furthermore, some men say that they would "never have had the nerve" to get married if they had been sober. Alcohol-induced courage seems to operate in the choice of a mate as well as in other crucial situations. Jackson A. Smith aptly observes that such marriages are "seldom destroyed because of the drinking; rather [they] are formed and endure as a manifestation of alcoholism."[1]

Thelma Whalen observed four types of wives of alcoholics in a family service agency and identified them on the assumptions that the wives of alcoholics, as well as their husbands, have poorly integrated personalities—that they choose an alcoholic husband on the basis of particular needs of their own, and that they are not "victims of circumstance," but "active participants in the creation of the problems which ensue."[2] The four types of wives of alcoholics which she identified are as follows:

1. *Suffering Susan.* This woman chose a marriage partner whom she knew would be difficult and who would gratify her own need for punishment and to be miserable. She has a low self-image and takes abuse and rejection as the normal state of the world's attitude toward her. In her marriage, she carries the primary responsibility of the family, is usually a model housekeeper, and a model of deportment. Suffering Susan interprets her situation as inevitable, as meant to be, blames no one for it, and lives with it fatalistically. She is likely to produce her

---

[1] "Problems in the Treatment of the Alcoholic," *Quarterly Journal of Studies on Alcohol,* Supplement 1 (November, 1961), 132.

[2] "Wives of Alcoholics: Four Types Observed in a Family Service Agency," *Quarterly Journal of Studies on Alcohol,* XIV (1953), 632-41.

own kind in her daughters and to produce dependent and sexually indecisive sons. Pastors, teachers, and social workers can help this family considerably by enabling the children to move out to more advantageous social situations such as camp. Companionship with older members of the opposite sex who can set a good example for them and enable the children to express their own private hostile feelings outside the home may also help stabilize the family. The wife herself needs encouragement, appreciation, and unconditional respect and kindness that will help her to raise her self-image.

2. *Controlling Catherine.* This woman chooses an inadequate man for a husband because of her own deep-seated need to dominate men. She distrusts and resents men generally, and an adequate man would be threatening. She takes charge of the relationship, is assured that she is the more adequate of the two, and usually chooses a man who is inferior in other ways. An example of this is a woman from a cultured family who married a man from the unskilled labor group of society. She had an M.A. degree, and he had an eighth-grade education. Intellectually, she was in the bright, normal range, and he in the slightly mentally retarded range. Economically, she had the ability to earn two or three times as much money as he could ever hope to earn. No amount of premarital counseling brought insight into this situation, and the marriage was effected nevertheless. Afterward, she took economic control of the family and the husband's alcoholism sustained the wisdom of her decision to control in the eyes of the community.

In pastoral counseling with such a family, the pastor can expect this controlling kind of wife to be hard and unforgiving, to project blame for the situation on the husband, and to "use" the pastor as a tool for bringing her husband "into line." It would be much better if such a woman had a woman counselor rather than a man counselor.

3. *Wavering Winifred.* This kind of woman is indecisive. She has "a need to be needed." She needs a husband who cannot

get along without her. This enables her to feel secure in the relationship. She has difficulty admitting her love for her husband, communicating her love to him, but no difficulty at all in continuing her loyalty to him because she cannot let him go. She will often say that she stays with him "for the children's sake," because "they need him and her together."

This wavering, indecisive kind of woman is more frequently married to an alcoholic than is the "sufferer" or the "controller." The strong factor in her relationship to her husband is her fidelity. A pastor can be a decisive, adequate, and exemplary man in her presence. This is good because she does not have to accept responsibility for the pastor as she does for her husband. Participation in Al-Anon will be exceptionally helpful to such a woman, because this group gives the wives of alcoholics a great deal of security, has clear and decisive guidance on the problems of living with an alcoholic, and is permissive and makes a minimum of demands. In other words, this woman has a weak sense of identity, wavers in her judgments, and needs an effective identity builder.

4. *Punishing Polly.* A fourth kind of wife of alcoholics is the woman who competes with men and punishes them when they are about to outdo her. She often is a career woman. A considerable number of such women are nurses. She is eager to bear financial responsibility. She rejects her home, children, and husband for interest in the more exciting world of competition. She chooses a husband who will relate to her as a boy to his mother. As Whalen says, "She is willing for her husband to have almost anything he wants—except his manhood." The husband's drinking is a way of asserting himself and escaping from this domination. The following clinical excerpt, given by Jackson A. Smith, tells of a successful and able attorney who

. . . married a girl who was socially prominent from a family that was financially secure. She was more aggressive sexually than the patient and before the honeymoon was over he was impotent. This he attributed to alcohol, but he continued to drink. Six years later he was literally dashing home at the end of the day for a drink. Once home he quickly drank himself into a stupor. Sometimes he ate dinner but, as often as not, he just drank.

However, he still scrupulously adhered to the pattern of not drinking in the morning or during the day unless he was to appear in court. He was convinced that as long as he was able to avoid a morning drink and to appear for work, he was not an alcoholic. His practice increased during this interval in spite of his drinking. It was not until his seventh year in practice that he began to drink during the day. During this same year he was first hospitalized after a bout.

This patient's law practice and his marriage evolved along with his alcoholism. . . . It was no surprise that when his wife demanded that he either stop drinking or she would sue for a divorce, he continued to drink.[3]

One wonders if the aggressive competence of this woman did not add to the professional insecurity of this man.

5. *Shrinking Sheila.* Jackson A. Smith identifies a fifth kind of marital choice on the part of the husband. Here the husband is aggressive and successful and the wife is reticent and socially inadequate. Using Whalen's nicknaming approach, we would call her the "Shrinking Sheila." She drinks in order "to get ready to go somewhere" or "be up to meeting her husband's friends." However, we have no extensive empirical studies of the alcoholic wife's effects on her husband and family. She is able to hide her drinking longer, particularly if she is not a working wife. One wonders if the addictive pattern in women does not develop additional addictions in the sexual sphere of their lives, particularly extramarital involvement and even prostitution. Some studies indicate that gambling, prostitution, and alcoholism operate in similar psychological relations.

Prior to the choice of a mate, the relationship between a man and a woman centers around play and irresponsible diversion from the heavier demands of life. However, the establishment of the home in the early family adjustments centers around work and the responsible commitments of life. The early family

---

[3]"Problems in the Treatment of the Alcoholic," *op. cit.*, p. 132.

adjustments of a new marriage present threatening demands, particularly to the man. Both husband and wife are called upon to be open and intimate with each other. This requires both the capacity and willingness to communicate verbally and clearly with each other.

Furthermore, early family adjustments require faithful fulfilment of promises and commitments, on a durable basis, between husband and wife. These commitments involve the clarification of the role of the husband and the place that the wife is to have in relation to him. All of these adjustments necessitate breaking away from the dependency upon their families of orientation—i.e., the in-laws—and learning to rely trustfully upon each other.

Consequently, little wonder is it that the first two years of marriage are anxiety-provoking in both subtle and obvious ways. Previously discussed research on the psychological problems which precondition a person toward alcoholism shows that the demands of marriage for intimacy, open communication, clearly defined roles, and so forth pose crucial threats to an individual husband and/or wife. Alcohol may temporarily anaesthetize or cause these threats to disappear for a season. Alcohol may be "used" to facilitate intimacy. A husband may not be able to speak his mind to his wife when he is sober and does so in a hurting and damaging way when he is drunk. A young wife may—instead of developing stomach trouble, biting her nails, or signaling her distress to her husband with her tears—turn to the facilitation of her anxiety with alcohol, the assuagement of her loneliness for her mother and father by drinking, or the retaliation against her husband for his neglect by becoming drunk.

Normally, young couples learn to communicate openly and intimately with each other, define clearly the spheres of their dependence and independence in relation to each other, agree through conversation concerning their specific roles as man and wife, and become independent of their "in-laws" as a part of the "establishment phase" of marriage. When these developmental tasks are not accomplished, vulnerability to an overuse of alcohol is the order of the day. Particularly is this true if the social drinking patterns of the couple are such as to expose them to the continued use of alcohol as a beverage.

The Advent of Children

In her unpublished doctoral dissertation at the University of Washington in 1955, Joan Jackson found that becoming a parent is one of the life events which is commonly associated with a sudden and marked increase in the number of symptoms listed by E. M. Jellinek, such as blackouts, morning drinking, "benders," daytime drinking bouts, loss of control, convulsions, tremors, and so forth.

This is particularly true for the father. The coming of the first child into the home is a crucial event. Dependent husbands tend to transfer their dependency from their mothers to their wives at the time of marriage. This adjustment succeeds in many instances until the birth of the first child. Then the mother shifts her protectiveness, solicitude, and companionship to the child. If she is the kind of "Wavering Winifred" who chose her husband because she "needed to be needed," then the coming of a child gives her someone else who needs her worse than a husband.

The sexual deprivation of the late stages of pregnancy and the dependency deprivation of the stage of infancy of the child tend to isolate the husband, and drinking may fill the void of his anxiety and loneliness. Some careful pastoral attention to couples at the birth of their children, in the form of small groups, home visitations, and personal counseling can do much to offset this kind of vulnerability of husband and wife. The interaction between husband and wife has been changed and needs to be understood, worked through, and readjusted.

Furthermore, alcoholism is associated with the birth of more children than the family economy and the earning power of husband and wife can afford. Little specific research is available on this. Clinical observation in low income families of a multiproblem variety reveals almost a monotonous record to validate this assumption. The identity of the father as an adequate man is weakened more and more as he is incapable of supporting his family. Also, the increased need for the care of the children limits the mother's capacity to work and earn money. The father is likely to use more and more of the family funds on alcohol. He retaliates by drinking more and more, getting revenge particularly on his employers from whom he receives censure because of his drinking and who fire him from his job. Alcohol, then, becomes the mechanism whereby he becomes totally dependent upon society. He may allow his family to become wards of welfare agencies. He may leave and then sneak back to spend a few days with his wife, and additional pregnancies may result.

The children of alcoholics need special attention here. Anne Roe made a study of the children of alcoholic parents who had been removed from the homes of their parents and reared in foster homes. She compared them with another control group of other foster children who did not have alcoholic parents. Her studies thoroughly explode the superstition that alcoholism is biologically inherited.[4]

Sons of alcoholic males find much difficulty in accepting their male roles in life unless they have the outside help of teachers, pastors, and other more adequate masculine examples around them. Daughters of alcoholic males, according to one observation, are forced to look to their mothers for both the father and mother role and, for this reason, have difficulty in separating masculine and feminine roles in later life. Also, feeble attempts by alcoholic fathers to exploit their daughters sexually, as well as their sons homosexually, have lasting traumatic effect on the development of effective relationships to the opposite sex. The Al-Anon family group studies reveal that children "are more affected than any other family member by living with an alcoholic."

The deep-running effect on a growing child of living with an

---

[4]"The Adult Adjustment of Children of Alcoholic Parents Raised in Foster Homes," *Quarterly Journal of Studies on Alcohol*, V (1944), 378-93.

alcoholic is confusion. When an alcoholic parent is sober, he has one kind of attitude toward the child. When he is drunk, another. When he is in a hangover, he has another. This flunctuating attitude confuses the child. The wife of an alcoholic alternates her treatment of the child as her moods toward her husband shift. Wives, according to Joan Jackson, "find themselves disliking, punishing, or depriving the children preferred by the father and those who resemble him." If a child is preferred by "or resembles the mother," he is "often hurt by the father." The child who wants to stay close to both parents is "caught in an impossible situation."[5] This ambivalent, contradictory treatment of the child is devastating to him in his attempt to find a clear path through life.

A Realistic Approach

The church and its pastors, Sunday School teachers, youth group leaders, ministers of music, and ministers of education are faced with a dilemma in ministering to the children of alcoholics. On the one hand, the child needs to have a strong, consistent, and basically happy spiritual leader with whom he can identify, like whom he can safely become, and in whom he can confide. On the other hand, he needs to respect and keep whatever is true, honorable, just, pure, lovely, and gracious, of any excellence and worthiness of praise, about his father or mother who may be alcoholic. The temptation of the religious leader is simply to exclude the alcoholic parent, reject him or her completely, and to attempt to take over a parental role in the life of the young person. These efforts are often doomed to fail because intuitively the child senses that this is wrong. Sooner or later, when the chips are down, the child will revert to being loyal to his parents and will break his relationship with the "do-good" approach characteristic of much sentimental religious effort to help the children of alcoholics.

---

[5]*Society, Culture, and Drinking Patterns,* eds. David J. Pittman and Charles R. Snyder (New York: John Wiley and Sons, 1962), p. 477.

A much more helpful and realistic approach to the child of the alcoholic parent is as follows:

1. Do not "splurge" sympathy on the child, but honestly assure him that he is not the only person who has had an alcoholic parent, nor will he be the last one. Other people have had this experience. Much has been learned about how to handle it. Much can be learned about how to handle it.

2. Begin teaching the child what is known about alcoholism. It is sick behavior. Alcoholism is one of the most insidious diseases known. The overwhelming mental urge to drink is beyond control. The alcoholic needs help and love; help and love should be wisely and carefully given. Other people who have alcoholic family members have gotten together.[6]

3. The pastor or religious worker should not allow himself, either consciously or subtly, to take over the parental role in the life of the young person. He should be available on an emergency standby basis to give help when the parent becomes inadequate and incompetent, and he should offer support, encouragement, and affection when the alcoholic is drunk and incompetent. As one nine-year-old boy said of his pastor, "I know that when my father gets to where he can't help me, my pastor is my friend and will pinch-hit."

4. If there are other children in the community who also have alcoholic parents, the pastor can help them relate to each other as friends. Sometimes an anonymous, casual get-together of these young persons to talk about what they have in common can be remarkably useful. One pastor found that in a subdivision where he himself lived, three families had one parent or another who were problem drinkers. Through his own children the pastor developed a sustaining friendship with the children of these three

[6]Two pamphlets that might be helpful in teaching young persons what they can and cannot do in relation to an alcoholic parent are *Living with an Alcoholic* and *Youth and the Alcoholic Parent,* available from Al-Anon Family Group Headquarters, P.O. Box 182, Madison Square Station, New York, N. Y., 10010, or from a local Alcoholics Anonymous headquarters.

families. His wife was a good neighbor and friend to the wives of these three problem-drinker husbands. On the regular routines of birthday parties, picnics, school carpools, and neighborhood yard maintenance chores, the pastor and his family maintained lasting relationships with these three families over a period of sixteen years.

Two of the three families were stabilized through a variety of community resources which the pastor mobilized in service to these three families. The third family had an unexpected windfall of inheritance money which fortunately was distributed wisely among the various members of the family. The children were cared for economically, the mother did not have to go to work, and the neighborhood provided much of the emotional consistency which the children needed. However, the father became more alcoholic and adopted drinking as a full-time vocation.

Strangely enough, two of of these three families were of a different denomination from that of the pastor. The church as an institution had little or no direct impact on this quiet but intense neighborhood drama. However, the pastor, as a neighbor, was involved significantly at deep levels of helpfulness.

Sometimes we get a candid view of the inner being of a young person by reading great American literature. One such insight into the son of an alcoholic can be found in an excerpt from Mark Twain's *Huckleberry Finn*. Huck Finn tells about his father's getting drunk:

> After supper pap took the jug, and said he had enough whisky there for two drunks and one delirium tremens. That was always his word. I judged he would be blind drunk in about an hour, and then I would steal the key, or saw myself out, one or 'tother. He drank, and drank, and tumbled down on his blankets, by-and-by; but luck didn't run my way. He didn't go sound asleep, but was uneasy. He groaned, and moaned, and thrashed around this way and that, for a long time. At last I got so sleepy I couldn't keep my eyes open, all I could do, and so before I knowed what I was about I was sound asleep, and the candle burning.

I don't know how long I was asleep, but all of a sudden there was an awful scream and I was up. There was pap, looking wild and skipping around every which way and yelling about snakes. He said they was crawling up his legs; and then he would give a jump and scream, and say one had bit him on the cheek—but I couldn't see no snakes. He started and run round and round the cabin, hollering "take him off! take him off! he's biting me on the neck!" I never see a man look so wild in the eyes. Pretty soon he was all fagged out, and fell down panting; then he rolled over and over, wonderful fast, kicking things every which way, and striking and grabbing at the air with his hands, and screaming, and saying there was devils ahold of him. He wore out, by-and-by, and laid still a while, moaning. Then he laid stiller, and didn't make a sound. I could hear the owls and the wolves, away off in the woods, and it seemed terrible still. He was laying over by the corner. By-and-by he raised up, part way, and listened, with his head to one side. He says very low:

"Tramp—tramp—tramp; that's the dead; tramp—tramp—tramp; they're coming after me; but I won't go—Oh, they're here! don't touch me—don't! hands off—they're cold; let go—Oh, let a poor devil alone!"

Then he went down on all fours and crawled off begging them to let him alone, and he rolled himself up in his blanket and wallowed in under the old pine table, still a-begging; and then he went to crying. I could hear him through the blanket.

By-and-by he rolled out and jumped up on his feet looking wild, and he see me and went for me. He chased me round and round the place, with a clasp-knife, calling me the Angel of Death and saying he would kill me and then I couldn't come for him no more. I begged, and told him I was only Huck, but he laughed *such* a screechy laugh, and roared and cussed, and kept on chasing me up. Once when I turned short and dodged under his arm he made a grab and got me by the jacket between my shoulders, and I thought I was gone; but I slid out of the jacket quick as lightning, and saved myself. Pretty soon he was all tired out, and dropped down with his back against the door, and said he would rest a minute and then kill me. He put his knife under him, and said he would sleep and get strong, and then he would see who was who.[7]

[7]Sculley Bradley, Richmond Croom Beatty, E. Hudson Long (eds.), *The American Tradition in Literature* (New York: W. W. Norton & Company, Inc., 1956-61) II, pp. 282-83.

All children may not be able to accept such behavior as steadily as Huck seems to. The problem of identity—"seeing who is who"—is a shared desperation of both the alcoholic and his son or daughter. In this quest for identity the church in its ministry is called to see both the alcoholic and his children as persons made in the image of God, for whom Christ died, and as bona fide members of the human race and the people of God.

The Failure of Husband-Wife Communication

The processes of communication between husband and wife are important in understanding the kind of behavior that preconditions one or the other member of the family to alcoholism. Marriage normally means that husband and wife have intimate access to each other at every level of communication. These levels can be identified: the level of verbal speech; the level of nonverbal "signals" which are mutually understood as a private language of every couple; the level of commonly accepted family rituals that give security, such as eating and playing family games; the level of trust, self-respect, and mutually agreed-upon covenants; and, finally, the level of tender love and committed warmth which expresses itself utimately in happy sexual union between husband and wife.

In husband-wife interaction, clear communication begins with the establishment of a clear covenant as to what they intend to mean to each other on an enduring basis throughout life. The absence of adequate premarital guidance or example in the home, the school, and the church leaves young people to enter marriage on the basis of hazy, confused, sentimental covenants. The process of trial and error becomes their major means of learning about marriage. The couple that has other adults around to offer encouragement, coaching, and fellowship during the learning process is fortunate and unusual.

For better or for worse, couples hack their way through difficulties alone. This aloneness doubles the importance of their being able to communicate with and to sustain each other. If inbred inabilities to communicate, emotional immaturities, and sheer fear and anxiety prevent a couple from trusting each other, and if these difficulties are compounded by unfortunate incidents and accidents to increase the distrust, then the couple tends to withdraw from each other into isolation and loneliness. This has been called "the stage of private misunderstanding" in the process of marriage conflict. At this stage the couple is estranged from each other and does not have access to helpful or hindering outsiders who either can catalyze or complicate the failures of communication.

At this stage, the couple will begin signaling the other member of the marriage partnership with various kinds of "illness" signals. An already existing physical illness may become the means of staying in touch with the marital partner. The stress and strain of the emotional situation may bring psychosomatic disorders into being. Predominantly psychic symptoms of indecision, depression, persecution, or hyperactivity may be the route that the distress takes.

In the choice of symptoms, excessive drinking of alcohol is one of the most common ways of signaling distress to one's partner. The husband, instead of coming home at the regular time, will stop by a bar for a few drinks. When he gets home, he is "loaded." The wife who is prone to drink will do so in order to "get ready for the ordeal of silence" with her husband. She may, if they have social engagements that evening, drink in order to brace herself for the social demands of the evening and to "put up appearances" before her friends and relatives. In both instances, the drinking is at one and the same time a facilitation of the loneliness caused by the private misunderstanding and failure of communication and a way of "getting through" the immediate stress.

The average church situation tends to compound, rather than to alleviate, this private misunderstanding between husband and wife. Most of our churches are composed of middle class people who put a high premium on "respectability" and the normative-ness of "not having any big problems." Even slightly deviant behavior is a taboo subject insofar as discussion in the church is concerned. Churchgoing itself may be a way of keeping up appearances, even when severe distress exists at home.

The astute pastor, Sunday School teacher, or deacon, however, can offset this respectability mania within the average church. Reflections of an understanding and considerate feeling toward people who are tempted to drink too much—given in the pulpit, a Sunday School class, or in private conversation—can often open the way for isolated husbands or wives to convey their distress privately to the pastor or teacher. Group discussions of the difficulties of marital adjustments with couples in the first five years of marriage often provide a starting place for a later private conversation with the isolated individual.

Private conversations in themselves do much toward relieving the necessity for the use of alcohol as a means of assuaging the loneliness created by a misunderstanding in marriage. In many instances alcohol is a substitute for the community of an effective marriage—an ineffective and dangerous substitute. It relieves temporarily, but complicates the possibilities of a more durable solution. A personal and trustworthy relationship to a pastor, a teacher, or a friend in the church can be a more effective and safer substitute for the failure of communication in the marriage. As such, it can go a long way toward eliminating the necessity for alcohol as an assuagement, a signal, and a substitute in marital failures of communication.

Cumulative Crisis

E. M. Jellinek describes alcoholism as a progressive disease, requiring from ten to fifteen years to progress to its worst stage, although it may escalate much more rapidly than this.

Joan Jackson has studied this same progressive process in its impact on the family. In 1951 she gathered her data from verbatim recordings of meetings of a family group of Alcoholics Anonymous known as the Al-Anon Family Group. She focused her studies primarily on the actions and attitudes of the wives of alcoholics. In 1961 she did a follow-up study.

Her methods of study were intensive interviews, psychological tests, and the study of a control group of persons who had no direct family experience with alcoholism.[8] Miss Jackson identifies seven progressive stages in the cumulative crisis of alcholism— successive crises that arise as the family seeks to adjust to the presence and behavior of an alcoholic husband and father.

Before these seven stages are enumerated, however, some attention needs to be given to a profile of the marriage at its beginning. Most of the men in these marriages were social drinkers at the time of marriage. A few of them already were alcoholics, but they hid this from their prospective wives. They would drink a little on dates, or they might not drink at all when with their future wives. They kept their fiancées away from friends and relatives who might tell of their excessive drinking. Characteristically, the relatives and friends who did manage to meet the fiancée were those who looked upon marriage as a sort of therapeutic strategy for settling the husband down, with the hope that "marriage would straighten him out." For this reason, they said nothing about the drinking. In only a very small number of cases did the fiancée know of her husband's alcoholism. In these cases, the women had little or no idea of what alcoholism is. There was little or no preparation for marriage at all, and no knowledge of alcohol in relation to marriage.

The church is responsible for knowing those whom it marries well enough to make the drinking behavior of the couple an open matter before marriage. However, if pastor and church are so rigid in their attitudes about drinking that this matter is a totally taboo subject, then the church is rendered ineffective from the outset. However, education about alcohol and alcoholism should be a part of effective premarital counseling for couples who are married by pastors and have some relation to the church.

[8]"The Adjustment of the Family to the Crisis of Alcoholism," *Quarterly Journal of Studies on Alcohol*, XV, No. 4 (December, 1954), 562-86.

In identifying the seven stages of postmarital adjustment of the family to the crisis of alcoholism, Miss Jackson gives thorough clinical descriptions. I have given brief names to each of the phases in order that they may be more easily remembered.

Stage 1: The "Perfectly Normal" Facade Phase.—Jackson describes this phase as follows: "Incidents of excessive drinking begin and, although they are sporadic, place strains on the husband-wife interaction. In attempts to minimize drinking, problems in marital adjustment not related to drinking are avoided." The members of the family, particularly the wife, initially deny that any problem exists. As the incidents of excessive drinking multiply, the wife particularly feels the need to "put up a front" and to define the situation as one of those things which is thoroughly understandable and perfectly normal. Between drinking bouts, efforts are doubled and redoubled to be "nice" and "ideal" with each other. The main mechanism of this phase of marital adjustment seems to be denial and rationalization.

Stage 2: The "Frantic" Phase.—Excessive drinking incidents multiply, and the family becomes socially isolated. The isolation intensifies the importance of things that happen in the family and between husband and wife. "Behavior and thought become drinking-centered. Husband-wife adjustment deteriorates and tension rises." However, the wife frantically tries to keep the original family structure even though it is disrupted with each episode of drinking. The franticness of the situation begins to show in emotional disturbances of the children.

Stage 3: The "What's-the-Use" Phase.—Here Miss Jackson says that the family gives up attempts to control the drinking and begins to behave in a manner geared to relieve tension rather than to achieve long-term ends. The disturbance of the children becomes more marked. There is no longer an attempt to support the alcoholic in his roles as husband and father. The wife begins to worry about her own sanity and about her own inability to make decisions or to act to change these situations. This is despair, accompanied by the depression of the wife, marked by indecision, and often characterized by her turning to her pastor, her Sunday School teacher, her close friend, or her parents. She has many decisions to make about the care of the children, the financial support of the family, and the control of the husband's behavior. She can no longer defend him before her friends or her children. He is defenseless. She can no longer make excuses for him or put up a front in his behalf. She has been embarrassed beyond the point of no return.

If pastors, teachers, and other helping members of the church take the attitude that the wife is totally responsible for the errant behavior of the husband, her depression will simply be increased and their relationship to her broken. If they take the attitude that the husband is totally responsible and that the wife and children are to be protected from an insufferable sinner, then the church itself will tend to take over the role of the wife in the situation and further weaken the possibilities of the husband's getting help for his difficulties.

However, if the church will blame no one, but look upon this situation as one in which responsibility is to be distributed as it would be in the case of any other illness, then, possibly, some realistic help can be gotten for the family. The wife can be advised to contact the pastor or another responsible person of the church when the husband becomes drunk again. Then, medical help can be gotten to him, and the isolation of the family can be overcome dramatically at the time of the next crisis. The wife can be encouraged to become a member of Al-Anon and can be given literature concerning the interaction of the wife with the husband who is alcoholic.[9]

Stage 4: The Stage of "The Great Takeover."—At this stage, Miss Jackson says that "the wife takes over control of the family

---

[9]The Al-Anon Family Group Headquarters publishes several articles in pamphlet form: *The Alcoholic Husband: A Message to Wives; Dos and Don'ts for the Wives of Alcoholics; Living With an Alcoholic.* For the children: *Youth and the Alcoholic Parent.* For the in-laws: *To the Mother and Father of an Alcoholic.* See footnote 6, p. 84.

and the husband is seen as a recalcitrant child. Pity and strong protective feelings largely replace the earlier resentment and hostility. The family becomes more stable and organized in a manner to minimize the disruptive behavior of the husband. The self-confidence of the wife begins to be rebuilt." However, this new stability marks a total shift of roles on the part of husband and wife. The survival of the family is temporarily assured because the wife has accepted full responsibility for the family. Jackson A. Smith in another article indicates that "in some instances complete reversal of the usual marital roles may occur, i.e., the wife works, the husband runs the household, does all the cooking, and most of the drinking. It may require a year or more to bring this change about, but once it happens, the couple may be much more compatible."[10]

The wife may gain certain indirect satisfactions from being the dominant member of the family, as has already been indicated. If this situation of reversed roles meets conscious or unconscious needs of the wife, the likelihood of the husband becoming chronically alcoholic is very high. However, if the wife in this circumstance decides that her husband must "shape up or ship out," refuses to supply him with any more alcohol, and demands that he take his role as husband, then the marriage faces another crisis which ushers in the fifth stage of the crisis in husband-wife interaction.

Stage 5: The Stage of "Outside Intervention."—In this stage, according to Miss Jackson, the wife separates from her husband if she can resolve the problems and conflicts surrounding this action. This means that the family of procreation has failed in its attempts to deal with the problem of alcoholism in the husband. Hostility and guilt, that duet of indecision, have finally given way to hopelessness, and the decision has been made on the basis of the hopelessness. Some wives may separate from their husbands as a means of shaking them to reality. Sometimes

---

[10]Jackson A. Smith, "Problems in the Treatment of Alcoholics," *Quarterly Journal of Studies on Alcohol*, Supplement No. 1 (November, 1961), 132.

separation from his wife will bring the husband to a jolting sense of reality and provoke something of a sense of need for outside help. However, this is a hazardous course to count upon as a sure thing. In any event, when an alcoholic husband and his wife separate, outside forces are called upon to intervene. What are some of these intervening agents?

The first and most common is the mother and father of the alcoholic himself. Many times the dependency of the alcoholic on his wife has been shifted back to its original source, namely, the mother. However, her attempts to control him simply do not work. He continues to defy her authority and ignores her pleas and moralisms. Many times it is parents of the alcoholic who bring him to the attention of the pastor and the church.

Another outside intervening agent is the police. The alcoholic gets into trouble with the law. He is arrested for drunken driving or disorderly conduct, or he may be caught trying to steal more money for more alcohol. The in-laws and the wife will be tempted to pay his fine and have him released in order to protect the family from embarrassment. They would be much better advised to let him profit by his own experience and accept responsibility for his own behavior. Then they might seek medical intervention for him in the event that he is allowed to go free or is given a short sentence.

The best kind of outside intervention comes when the alcoholic can be persuaded to seek help from the Alcoholics Anonymous group or from similar groups established within the church. Alcoholics Anonymous has had better results intervening in the lives of alcoholics than has anyone else. Wives, parents, pastors, and lay church leaders can all serve as "ministers of introduction" to get the alcoholic into AA.

In most instances, however, medical intervention is greatly needed at this point. If those closely related to the alcoholic can see his difficulties as an illness and get him to a doctor, they may open the way for further kinds of help later. A considerable amount of decisive authority can be mobilized to see to it that the alcoholic gets medical care, even against his own will. Not all sick men (no matter what the disease) go willingly to a doctor. There seems to be something in American definitions of masculinity that argues against early medical attention for any kind of disease.

Stage 6: The "I-Can-Get-Along-Without-You-Very-Well" Stage. Here Miss Jackson says that "the wife and children reorganize as a family without the husband." They decide that they can get along without him. In effect, he is told directly or indirectly to "get lost," inasmuch as he is already lost anyway.

This is the same kind of situation that exists in any divorced family, except that it is worse. Divorce does not completely sever all relationships between husband and wife and between father and children. But, the family that has been disrupted by alcoholism lives in fear that the drunken husband may come in upon them when they are sleeping. He may either call or appear at the place of work of the wife. He may seek to contact the children at school, or at other places where the mother is not with them. He may show up at public gatherings which the family attends. He may even show up drunk at church.

The church often becomes a substitute for the absent father when the family reorganizes without him. The ministering church has the responsibility, along with other institutions of society such as the public school, for filling up the empty places in the lives of children who have lost their father by any means. The church also has a responsibility of ministering to the wife and children in their guilt about having deserted the alcoholic father. At any rate, the family becomes reorganized and is able to survive without the father.

Stage 7: The Stage of "The Happy Reunion."—Stage six is really one alternative in the process of interaction between an alcoholic and his family. The assumption is that the family is reorganized in two parts, with the husband being eliminated. Stage seven is the second alternative, where the whole family is reorganized with the husband included. This takes place when the husband achieves sobriety and returns to his family. However, the other problems in adjustment, not related directly to drinking and hitherto unrecognized and unmet, now have to be dealth with forthrightly. Jackson says that "for the wife and husband facing a sober marriage after many years of an alcoholic marriage, the expectations of what marriage without alcoholism will be are unrealistically idealistic and the reality of marriage almost inevitably brings disillusionment." All does not go perfectly well, and the roaring lion of alcoholism has turned into a thousand mice of other problems which have to be dealt with on a day-to-day basis, just as is true in any other marriage.

Also, the children have the difficult task of reorienting themselves to their father in the face of the memory of things that he had said and done to them in the past. The possibility of older children leaving is a live option for easing this tension. The possibilities of girls marrying early as a way out of the situation are high. Here it is that the supportive institutions of the community such as church, school, Alcoholics Anonymous, and Al-Anon, have a major continuing ministry to provide for all members of the family.

These continuing responsibilities call for a systematic approach by the church to a practical program of discharging responsibilities among its members for dealing with the problem of alcoholism. This is the subject of the next chapter.

VI

Alcohol and Types of Conversion

C. Roy Woodruff, Coauthor*

Christians are concerned with converting persons to belief in Jesus Christ. Conversion, one of the goals of evangelism, is that decisive event in which a person turns from his "bondage, sorrow, and night" and enters freely into the grace of God. The church has proclaimed this truth. It has yet to explore clinically the various meanings which the conversion experience has for different people. The church that takes conversion seriously takes equally seriously the uniqueness of those persons to whom it speaks.

Each person's life situation shapes the meaning of conversion for him. This is especially true for the alcoholic. Conversion has a special meaning for him because it turns him from an ultimately destructive compulsion to an ultimately constructive commitment. The alcoholic's conversion has a living significance that may not be found in other conversions. This radical transformation has many facets. This chapter is a consideration of the various aspects of conversion in the experience of a variety of alcoholic addicts.

Kinds of Conversion

Nonreligious conversion.—Harry M. Tiebout, psychiatrist and past president of the National Committee on Alcoholism, has

---

*Doctoral candidate under the author's supervision; also graduate Teaching Fellow, Department of Psychology of Religion, Southern Baptist Theological Seminary, Louisville, Kentucky.

made valuable contributions to understanding the psychological conversion of an alcoholic. He defines conversion as "a psychological event in which there is a major shift in personality manifestation."[1] This defines that kind of conversion which we shall refer to as "nonreligious conversion." In nonreligious conversion the individual is transformed both in his self-concept and in his relationships to others. The psychosocial conversion remains on a psychological and social level. It is a horizontal, as opposed to a vertical, experience. There is a sense of release and a new direction in life, but no sense of transcendency, i.e., being lifted above the human situation.

Limited religious conversion.—Religious conversion may be defined as an event or process in which there is a major shift in the central focus of one's life by reason of a divine-human encounter. For the alcoholic the shift would be from alcohol to God. He no longer looks for "God-in-a-bottle." Howard J. Clinebell says, "It is, at least in part, because men have not found God elsewhere that they seek him in a bottle."[2] The personality may retain the same characteristics, but it expresses itself in a new context or frame of reference. The primary indication of this experience is its transcendent quality. The individual experiences a vertical or upward movement toward God and a downward movement from God which is absent from the psychosocial, nonreligious conversion.

Like the nonreligious conversion, however, the limited religious conversion does affect the person's self-concept and his relationships to his family, neighbors, employers, and fellow employees. He is more concerned with the lives of others. But the conversion is limited. The converted alcoholic equates his experience with God himself. He uses his conversion as a norm which he imposes upon all other alcoholics. This experience may

---

[1] "Conversion as a Psychological Phenomena in the Treatment of the Alcoholic," *Pastoral Psychology*, II, No. 13 (1951), 28.

[2] *Understanding and Counseling the Alcoholic* (New York: Abingdon Press, 1956), p. 149.

be described as redirection of his compulsions rather than release from his compulsions. Religion becomes a substitute for alcohol.

Comprehensive conversion.—The first two categories of conversion are inadequate and incomplete; comprehensive conversion is genuine conversion. The term "comprehensive" is used to convey the sense of being deeply felt, total, transforming, releasing, transcendent. It is similar to what Wieman calls "supreme conversion."[3] It emphasizes the central focus of life around the revelation of God. It breaks the power of compulsion, the bondage both to alcohol and "the law" of proud religiosity. It involves a total response of faith and not a partial response of religious hyperactivity. What Wieman leaves out—and what we stress— is the need for a "cornerstone" upon which God builds and around which man can mobilize his personal strengths for purposeful living. Comprehensive and genuine conversion is a dynamic process. Through redemption in Jesus Christ, the person feels both freedom and commitment, the power of personal action, and the presence of God in the fellowship of the Holy Spirit.

Three Case Studies

The case of Mr. Goode: A nonreligious conversion.—Mr. Goode is a fifty-year-old white man, a painter by trade. When he was three years old, his father died. Thereafter, the boy was reared in a strict home by his mother and was forced to go to Sunday School and church. As soon as he became old enough to get a job, he stopped attending church and began drinking. He married and continued to drink. His income was good, but, as his drinking became compulsive, he spent most of the money on liquor. His wife threatened to leave him if he did not stop drinking, but her warning had little effect. He refused to stop, she left, and he went on a six-month spree.

---

[3]Henry Nelson Wieman and Regina Westcott-Wieman, *Normative Psychology of Religion* (New York: Thomas Y. Crowell Company, 1935), p. 163.

Realizing that he had hit bottom and needed his wife, he submitted to her demands to stop. She came back, and he did not drink for two years. However, he was unhappy during this time because he wanted to drink but knew that his wife would leave if he did. Finally, he told her she "could go to hell," he was going to drink. She did not leave him.

Mr. Goode knew that he was a confirmed alcoholic, but he did not care; he had lost all self-respect.

One night Mr. Goode was driven home by one of his drinking buddies and got out of the car in a stupor. Living next to the Goodes was a young couple. As Mr. Goode started toward his house, he saw the young wife in front of her house. He turned toward her and, using crude language, tried to proposition her into sexual relationship. The young wife's husband heard him and came out of the house. Somehow, without conflict, they got Mr. Goode home.

The next morning Mr. Goode had no recollection of the incident, but his wife, the husband of the young woman, and several others who had heard him told him what he had said and done. Struck with a deep sense of shame and regret, he said, "I'm not that kind of man! If this is what alcohol makes me do, I'll never drink again."

That was over ten years ago, and he has not had a drink since then. He says that he has no desire to drink, but he knows that if he were to take one drink now, the desire would return and he would begin again.

Mr. Goode is now undergoing treatment for tuberculosis. A considerable percentage of alcholics have a history of tuberculosis, and there is probably some causal relationship between alcoholism and the disease. Alcoholism weakens the physical condition and makes the body less resistant to tubercular germs.

Also, Mr. Goode has a chronic brain syndrome as a result of excessive intoxication. It shows itself in mild episodes of euphoria and marked sentimentality, and the brain damage may influence his apparent lack of hostility. But it does not, at this point, interfere with his ability to relate to others or to continue his work. Mr. Goode has a pleasant, congenial personality and relates well to other patients, hospital employees, and the medical staff. He talks freely, but not compulsively, about his alcoholism. He becomes quite sentimental when describing a tender feeling.

Apparently, Mr. Goode has radically shifted his personality expression; he notes that his attitude toward other people has developed into one of concern for their problems and feelings. He gets pleasure out of helping others, and is no longer ego-centric, infantile, and self-centered, as he was when he was drinking. He is not a Christian, but he "tries to do right."

When one tries to determine the way in which brain damage affects the personality, a research problem arises. How should this effect on the personality be interpreted in the light of the theology of conversion?

Mr. Goode experienced a nonreligious conversion. His decision was a sudden, complete return to reality. His drunken behavior was not in line with his self-image. An intense sense of shame precipitated a radical personality transformation. His experience had all the ingredients of genuine conversion except the religious element. An awareness of God was not a part of his experience, nor is God deeply significant to him now. However, he says he knows something is missing in his life. An "existential vacuum"— an emptiness of purpose or meaning—remains.

The case of Mr. Wright: A limited religious conversion.—Mr. Wright is a fifty-two-year-old white male who is a carpenter by trade. His father died when Mr. Wright was seven years old, leaving the family in economic distress. His family was respected, but poor.

At age sixteen, Mr. Wright left home and went to the West Coast. He remained about a year, then went back East. In an eastern city he was noticed by a fight manager and began to box. He had lifted weights earlier and was quite strong and well built. Mr. Wright was successful at boxing, and he worked hard at it. At the time when he had a chance to go to the international

Golden Gloves competition, he became interested in professional wrestling and gave up boxing. Again, he was successful in wrestling and a leading contender for the title. He was defeated for the title in a close match. After this match, he became well known and was invited to many drinking parties. He married during this time and began to participate in the drinking until he became a habitual drinker. His wrestling career rapidly degenerated until he was out of it completely.

Mr. Wright then got a job as a carpenter and soon opened his own business. He went to Sunday School on two occasions and walked out both times when temperance was discussed. One night a friend, a former alcoholic, came by to see him, to share his salvation experience, and to talk with Mr. Wright about accepting Christ. Mr. Wright rejected this attempt to convert him. He says, "By that time I hated just about everybody."

One person whom the carpenter did not hate was an orphan boy who worked for him. Having no children, Mr. Wright took a personal interest in the boy. One afternoon the boy, walking down the highway, was hit by a car and killed. Mr. Wright was deeply shaken and stayed drunk for weeks after the incident. One night he came home drunk, and his wife faced him forthrightly with his intoxication. He was angered and hit his wife. At that moment Mr. Wright became aware of what he was doing to himself and others. He felt the pains of sorrow and shame. He confessed his sin before God, asked for help, and committed himself to God. Mr. Wright was drunk when he accepted Christ, and he has not had a drink in over twenty years.

Since his conversion, Mr. Wright has been extremely active as a Christian. He is closely identified with a local church. He habitually reads his Bible, prays, and witnesses every day. Supported in his activities by his wife, he has worked with the inmates of penal institutions and juvenile detention homes. Mr. Wright is interested in seeking to convert alcoholics to Christ and says that this is the only sure way that a person can give up alcohol.

The long-suffering faithfulness of Mrs. Wright is a remarkable fact in this experience. She stood by her husband as a companion and a Christian during difficult years. The affectionate solidarity of their present relationship is itself a witness to the reconciling grace of God.

Mr. Wright has a pattern of seeking excellence in almost everything he has begun, and his Christian life is no exception. He says that he is determined to be the best possible Christian, and he wastes no energy driving toward this goal. Although there is much to be respected about a strong stand, Mr. Wright's habitual and compulsive nature can be seen in his life as a Christian. He rigidly refuses to make a business contract with anyone who deals in the sale of alcohol or to employ anyone who is a known drinker. He has little use for AA, saying that human methods will not solve the alcohol problem. He has a good business and a comfortable home, but his particular conversion experience has limited him in a way which he admits but does not see as a disadvantage. He knows that if he were not "addicted" to Christianity, he would return to alcohol or some other form of addiction. Mr. Wright's compulsive personality in itself has remained unchanged.

The Case of Mr. Freeman: A comprehensive religious conversion.—Mr. Freeman is a thirty-five-year-old man who is now a Baptist minister. As an infant he was baptized into the Roman Catholic Church and grew up in a Catholic environment. However, he was never actively involved in the Catholic Church. As a result of his parents' divorce when he was six years old, Mr. Freeman was deprived of an adequate relationship with his father. He lived with his mother and saw his father only on occasions outside the home. Both his mother and father drank alcoholic beverages, and he recalls times when he saw them intoxicated. The use of alcohol was socially accepted in his environment. Mr. Freeman began to drink in early adolescence.

When Mr. Freeman was fifteen, his mother died. This deeply grieved him and left him without any meaningful parental relationship. He sought his relationships among his peers who, in a sense, became his family. With them, he began to drink heavily and frequently. He gambled and consorted with prostitutes, searching for something to make life worthwhile and meaningful. Both his inner struggle and his need for his mother appeared two years after his mother's death when he went to the church and prostrated himself before the virgin Mary and prayed for help. He found no help from the church.

Mr. Freeman's initial conversion came when he was with friends, preparing for a carnival celebration. Intoxicated, Mr. Freeman, in a moment of self-revelation, realized the meaninglessness of his own life and of all that was going on around him. He felt ashamed of his immoral behavior. He said to his friends: "We are not seeking the meaning of life in the right way. We must find a better way to give ourselves purpose." One of his friends agreed with him and suggested that they find a Bible and begin to read it. They went immediately to the house of a judge who was a Protestant and asked him for a Bible. He gave them one and helped them understand how to use it. This was Mr. Freeman's first step toward a comprehensive conversion.

Soon after this experience Mr. Freeman became ill. Confined to bed for several months, he read his Bible and thought about what it meant to be a Christian. There was no priest in his town. A Catholic nun who lived nearby took an interest in him and visited him often. She tried to explain what it meant to be a Catholic Christian and to help him back into the church. Mr. Freeman was careful not to let her see the Protestant Bible he was reading until he realized that he could not honestly hide this from her. He waited until her next visit and made a point of reading the Protestant Bible as she came in. She was shocked and hurt by this and told Mr. Freeman that he should not be reading such a thing. He told her that he could see no difference in the Protestant and Catholic Bibles and that he was going to continue to read it. This broke the relationship with the nun.

From that point on Mr. Freeman moved consistently in the

Christian life and followed the call to become a minister. He realized that alcohol and his immoral behavior were futile attempts to give meaning to his life. The Christian faith gave him a central purpose in life and opened the door to growth and spiritual maturity. Although there was a definite point at which conversion occurred, Mr. Freeman's experience led him beyond his initial "turning" and into a dynamic, genuine pilgrimage as a Christian. He is a warm, conscientious person who is open to new forms of learning and to new relationships. He is committed to Jesus Christ, but his commitment has given him a sense of freedom and release. His relationship to God is through grace rather than law or "works." Mr. Freeman's experience has been a comprehensive religious conversion in which he is still actively involved, becoming an informed, mature minister of the gospel of Jesus Christ. He has been free of alcohol for fifteen years.[4]

The Meaning of Surrender

The Necessity of Surrender.—Harry M. Tiebout strongly emphasizes the necessity of surrender as a prerequisite to conversion. He discusses one converted alcoholic who, "after trying to manage his own case to his own near ruination, . . . surrendered to the need for help, after which he entered a new state of mind which has enabled him to remain sober."[5]

Defiant individuality and grandiosity, says Tiebout, block surrender. These must be overcome in order for an alcoholic to surrender. Surrender is defined as "a moment when the unconscious forces of defiance and grandiosity actually cease to function effectively. When that happens the individual is wide open to reality; he can listen and learn without conflict and fighting

---

[4]The authors acknowledge and give thanks to the persons whose life stories are recorded here. The necessary permissions for using this information have been received and all identifying data have been anonymously reported.

[5]"The Act of Surrender in the Therapeutic Process with Special Reference to Alcoholism," *Quarterly Journal of Studies on Alcohol,* X (1949), 50.

back."[6] This spiritual event is demonstrated vividly in the case of Mr. Wright whose defiance and grandiosity were shattered when he, a boxer and wrestler, degenerated to the point of hitting a woman. This shattering made surrender possible. However, the grandiosity was equated with his conversion experience later. Genuine humility remained absent.

The *act* of surrender must be followed by a *state* of surrender, which is the persisting capacity to accept reality without obligation or fatalism. Tiebout combines both the act and state of surrender into a single phenomenon which he calls the "surrender reaction."

Tiebout points out that for some "there seems to occur a phenomenon which might be called 'selective surrender.' After the effects of the initial surrender experience have worn away, the individual reverts to being much the same person he was before, except that he does not drink and so has no battle on that line."[7] This would apply, in some measure, to the experience of Mr. Wright, who remains compulsive and habitual in his dependence upon the rituals of the religious life.

Surrender and submission.—It is important to distinguish between surrender and submission. Tiebout indicates that submission is a conscious, superficial yielding in which tension continues. This may be understood better from the point of view that submission is a "part" rather than a total function of the person. Andras Angyal, a practicing psychiatrist, has noted that personality disturbance occurs when a "part function" disrupts the total function of the individual. As a "part function," submission is a half-hearted, tension-producing expression which denies the need for a totally functioning personality.[8]

Surrender, on the other hand, is unconscious and provides release from tension. It may be noted that Mr. Goode "submitted"

[6]*Ibid.*, p. 54.
[7]*Ibid.*, pp. 55-56.
[8]*Foundations for a Science of Personality* (New York: The Commonwealth Fund, 1941), p. 329.

to his wife's demands and stopped drinking for two years, only to return to alcoholism. It was not until he had "surrendered" that he was able to stop drinking completely. In contrast to submission, surrender is a comprehensive, wholehearted expression of the totally functioning person.

The Paradox of Surrender.—The "surrender reaction" is paradoxical in nature. The battle against alcoholism can be won only by giving up. There must be more than a "cease fire" agreement or a compromising self-negotiation. Unconditional surrender in the face of the reality of defeat will alone bring victory. In an article on "Treatment of Alcoholics," Martin D. Kissen says:

"Surrender" is the process by which a patient recognizes and accepts the fact that any time he takes any quantity of alcohol, his particular pattern of binge drinking will follow sooner or later. This, of course, implies rather paradoxically that the only way to defeat the consequences of alcoholism is to surrender to the fact that he cannot ingest any alcohol.[9]

Here is the age-old paradox that only when one loses his life to that which is beyond himself can he find his life.

The alcoholic could quickly identify with these lines by Robert Frost:

> Something we were withholding made us weak
> Until we found out that it was ourselves
> We were withholding from our land of living,
> And forthwith found salvation in surrender.[10]

The shame-axis approach to surrender.—Although Tiebout speaks at length about the "surrender reaction" of the alcoholic who faces reality and accepts it, he does not plunge deeper to explore the emotional state which makes the person open to surrender. Our case studies reveal *shame* as an important dynamic at work in the conversion experience. Shame brought the

---

[9]*Quarterly Journal of Studies on Alcohol,* Supplement No. 1 (November, 1961), 104.

[10]"The Gift Outright," *In the Clearing* (New York: Holt, Rinehart, and Winston, 1962), p. 31.

alcoholics into reality. Shame made them see themselves as they really were. Their self-image was not in line with their behavior. This split revealed their lack of identity, real or pseudo. As one character in a modern play puts it, the alcoholic jolts to the bottom and realizes that he is "a nothin' man with nothin' special in his name." He is ashamed. Our alcoholic friends, unable to mobilize any defense against utter shame, had no real alternative except surrender. The depth and direction of their sense of shame seem to be the strength of their conversions.

Russell L. Dicks indicates that the alcoholic comes equipped with a sense of shame. He says, "The alcoholic has low self-esteem, loss of a sense of personhood, loss of a sense of dignity."[11] This makes the person retreat into the hard shell of alcoholism. He feels threatened and defensive. He cannot think much of others when he thinks so little of himself.

A. H. Maslow, professor of psychology at Brandeis University, states that those who do not live up to their potential and who betray themselves "perceive in a deep way that they have done wrong themselves and despise themselves for it."[12] Out of this experience will come either neurosis or growth and renewal of courage and self-respect. To despise oneself is to possess a deep, shattering sense of shame for oneself.

Helen Merrell Lynd in her book *Shame and the Search for Identity* has carefully explored the characteristics of shame. Much of what she says applies to the conversion of an alcoholic. "Being taken unpleasantly by surprise," says Miss Lynd, "the impossibility of order behavior, the sudden sense of exposure, of being unable to deal with what is happening, characterize shame. It is as if a self of which we were not aware makes us unable to grasp the situation and to control what we do."[13] What Miss Lynd

---

[11]"The Alcoholic and a Sense of Dignity," *Social Action*, XXIII (May, 1957), 9.

[12]*The Self*, ed. Clark E. Moustakas (New York: Harper and Row, 1956), p. 236.

[13](New York: Science Editions, Inc., 1961), p. 34.

says fits two of our cases exactly when she describes shame as the reaction a person has when what is exposed is incongruous with his self-image. Mr. Wright had seen himself as a strong, manly person. In his experience of shame he saw himself hitting his wife, a woman. This shattered his pseudo-masculine dream world. Mr. Goode had seen himself as a respectable, decent person. In his experience of shame he saw himself being crude and disrespectful to a young wife. The suddenness of their exposure brought them to spontaneous surrender. Since shame is a personal event involving the whole person, the only way it can be transcended is by surrendering the whole person.

The guilt-axis approach.—The most accurate approach to the problem of surrender and conversion is on the shame-axis rather than the guilt-axis, which is the one usually used with the alcoholic. Guilt is certainly involved. Guilt, however, involves much less of the total sense of exposure and emptiness which characterize shame. It is important for the family and friends of an alcoholic to know that they must not cover up for the shamefulness of the alcoholic's behavior, however embarrassing it is to them. The alcoholic's powers of retaliation through the compulsive use of alcohol grab hold of *his family's sense of shame and need for respectability and use it as a key to free himself from his own sense of shame.* The family plainly should not let this happen. To do so lowers rather than raises the bottom the alcoholic must hit. This bottom is a total sense of shame, not just uneasy and anxious guilt. The experience of shame may be the key which opens his way to surrender and conversion.

The Problem of Identity

Identity Diffusion.—One of the common traits shared by our three cases is a lack of positive identity. All exhibit unrest and dissatisfaction with their lives. The alcoholic is characterized by such expressions as "life has no meaning," and "this is not really me." He has fallen short of even the glory of man, has not realized his own potential, and lives in a state of self-derogation.

Maslow points out that in self-concept it is a very serious thing

. . . for each person to recognize vividly and poignantly, each for himself . . . that every falling away from species-virtue, every crime against one's own nature, every evil act, *every one without exception records itself* in our unconscious and makes us despise ourselves. . . . If we do something we are ashamed of it registers to our discredit, and if we do something honest or fine or good it registers to our credit. The net results ultimately are either one or the other—either we respect and accept ourselves or we despise ourselves and feel contemptible, worthless, and unlovable.[14]

When one can understand this about human nature in general, he can begin to understand the loss of self-respect characteristic of the alcoholic. Many alcoholics' lives are a collection of chronic failures, false starts, brilliant successes, and sudden failures. Others' are an uninterrupted chain of failures. The alcoholic knows he has done wrong to himself and others, and he despises himself for it. The self-derogation results in the chronic identity-diffusion characteristic of alcoholics.

This theory of the identity diffusion of the alcoholic received further support from a study of alcoholics and homosexuals by Robert J. Gibbins and Richard H. Walters. These men concluded that alcoholics have difficulty with sexual identity. However, the alcoholic does not necessarily identify with the wrong sex. He fails to identify firmly with either sex.[15] It is more than likely that the almost complete lack of adequate paternal care in each case cited contributed much to their identity diffusion.

Negative Identity.—This "despised self" attitude, which is characteristic of identity diffusion, may lead to what Erik Erikson calls the "choice of a negative identity."[16] This is a perversely based identity in which the individual flatly and totally capitu-

---

[14]Maslow, *op. cit.*, p. 234.
[15]"Three Preliminary Studies of a Psychoanalytic Theory of Alcohol Addiction," *Quarterly Journal of Studies on Alcohol*, XXI (1960), 618-41.
[16]"Identity and the Life Cycle," *Psychological Issues*, I, no. 1, monograph 1 (1959), 129-32.

lates as a self to the negative characteristics with which he has been confronted. Preaching at him and "trying to get him to see" himself as a worm is out of time and joint. He sees this, admits it, and gets attention by being this. Although full-blown alcoholism occurs only in adults, this is a kind of "teen-age-bad-boy" syndrome in adults. Erikson says that "many a late adolescent [which is a chronic stage for the alcoholic] if faced with continuing diffusion, would rather *be nobody or somebody bad, or indeed, dead—and this totally, and by free choice—than be not-quite-somebody.*"[17] Erikson's reference to death would coincide with the theory that alcoholism is a chronic suicide. Erikson makes good sense when one sees how an alcoholic will usually resist help from "good" people.

When the alcoholic firmly establishes his negative identity, alcoholism becomes a vocation, a calling, a way of life. Jamie, in Eugene O'Neill's *Long Day's Journey into Night,* has such a vocation. Although he has talent as an actor, he never succeeds at acting or at anything constructive. Jamie's only success is with alcohol and prostitutes. His self-identity is completely negative, and his vocation becomes the fulfilling of his negative identity.

In the "surrender reaction" the alcoholic regresses to the lowest level of identity loss. He is a child of darkness confronting the nothingness of a Nirvana without an identity of his own. Even his negative identity is surrendered at that point. As Biff says of his dead father in Arthur Miller's *Death of a Salesman,* "He never knew who he was." However, at the extremities of regression the alcoholic finds his only firm foundation for a renewal of life and determined progression. This giving in to the pull of regression is what Erikson calls the "rock-bottom attitude."[18]

The constructive aspect of shame is that the exposure of oneself as he is can lead to the discovery of one's own identity. When the alcoholic hits bottom and sees who he is and the possibility of what he may become, he is saturated with shame. It is a painful

[17]*Ibid.*, p. 132.
[18]*Ibid.*, p. 133.

experience, but it is his only hope for recovery. To maintain sobriety, the alcoholic must gain a sense of identity.

Conversion terminates regression and initiates progression. Progression involves both the personal resolve of the alcoholic and his willingness to surrender to outside help. Then his ego identity may become sufficient for his needs. He may begin to enjoy sobriety and enter the gates of a new life.

Deprivation and Parental Inadequacy

Each of the alcoholics studied in this chapter lost his father early in life either by death or by divorce. This chasm was not filled at the time by adequate substitutes and, in the case of nonreligious conversion, was never replaced either by a group or by a leader of any kind. In the case of the incomplete religious conversion, the emptiness was filled by the assumption of religious leadership on the part of the man himself. He himself became his own father-figure. No other man could take his own place in his life. In the case of the complete religious conversion, there was an interesting movement during adulthood from one kind of substitute for the absent father to another: first, the group of fellow teen-agers; second, the mother-nun of the Catholic faith became the authority figure; finally, a continuous succession of men teachers and leaders provided an adult leadership in the life of the continually growing convert.

This suggests the vital function of religion in the life of the alcoholic as in the life of any other deprived person: religion fills in the gap left by death, defection, divorce, and all the other relationship-breaking powers of life. The fellowship of believers supplies emotional nutriments left unsupplied by the family and other community structures such as the neighborhood, the school, and the job. Religion does not become a mere substitute for deprivation. Rather, it strengthens and nourishes the deprived individual in such a way that his deprivation does not rule out continued growth and an abundant life.

Further, the loss of their fathers affected these three men's relationships to their mothers and wives. The sense of shame came over the first convert when he received acceptance and help from the husband of the woman whom he had insulted and forgiveness and help from his own wife. The second convert was overcome by shame when he realized what he had done to his wife by hitting her. The third convert was first nurtured by the image of Mary, the mother of Jesus; next, given special guidance by a Catholic nun, and finally, given continuous support and encouragement by his wife. The establishment of openness and accessibility to women *as adults* seemed to be the channel for resolving the hunger and deprivation. In all three instances the act and state of surrender was either initiated or sustained, or both initiated and sustained, in relation to adult women.

The primary identity of Mr. Goode is that of a reformed alcoholic. He thinks of himself in these terms. While this identity has the advantage of leaving him open to further growth and development, it has the disadvantage of a remaining strand of diffusion. Mr. Goode represents this by saying, "I know something is missing in my life." His goals and purposes are hazy. He has nothing outside of himself with which to identify.

The primary identity of Mr. Wright is that of a "reformed alcoholic and witnessing Christian." This identity has the advantage of giving Mr. Wright a central focus around which to organize his life. He has thus a definite purpose in life. But it has the disadvantage of leaving Mr. Wright a rigid, compulsive person who is addicted to religion. The religion is predominantly a "works" religion, one that demands much, affords a little, and comforts and satisfies not much. Further growth would be difficult for him to attain. He has become the teacher and does not appear receptive to new learning. This kind of person becomes arrogant and opinionated.

Evidently both of these men lack something the other has. Mr. Goode lacks a central focus and an eternal purpose in life. Mr. Wright is lacking a sense of release and freedom in life which leads to continuing growth. While Mr. Goode speaks of his need for spiritual growth and is a most tolerant person, Mr. Wright describes how he has achieved his spiritual status and is in a shell of satisfaction. Mr. Goode lives as one who is open to new experiences, although brain damage will inhibit his ability to learn from new experiences.

Since these two cases appear not to be wholly satisfactory solutions, perhaps the third category needs to be stressed. As already seen, the comprehensive religious conversion may be represented by the experience of Mr. Freeman. This conversion experience incorporates the advantages of both previous experiences without the disadvantages of either. Mr. Freeman was able to discover a cornerstone upon which to build his new life. He entered a sense of release and freedom which has led him enthusiastically toward further growth. Rather than being preoccupied with the past, he is resonant with joy in the present and hope for the future. He is a warm, considerate person with a positive identity. He imposes himself upon no one, but he leaves himself open to almost everyone.

In this chapter we have been exploring the variations of alcoholic conversions and the lives in which these conversions have taken place. We have seen the meaning of dynamics of surrender and the identity diffusion characteristic of alcoholism. The primary thrust of this study is that both the nonreligious and the limited religious conversions are incomplete. They are not total conversions in that both are limited. What is needed is a dynamic, genuine, comprehensive conversion which is channeled through surrender, transcends shame, provides freedom, and gives the individual an identity which is grounded in the eternity of God. The entire fellowship of the church must be sensitive to this need in the life of the converted alcoholic and give him room to grow as a Christian without the stumblingblocks of spiritual exploitation placed in his way.

VII

The Church's Ministry

Opinion about alcohol and alcoholism in American culture is seldom unanimous. The contradictions, confusion, and competition revealed in the veritable Babel of voices are major contributors to the misuse of alcohol, to individual compulsions, and to the difficulty in treatment of alcoholism. Cutting one's way through this jungle of contradictions to bring order out of chaos is the prime responsibility of the churches and their ministers. Avoidance of this responsibility cannot be explained away by taking a hard party line in behalf of total abstinence, legal prohibition, social drinking, or even the disease concept of alcoholism. Each of these approaches brings varying degrees of results, but the hard legalism with which each is proclaimed further contributes to moral confusion in both church and community.

The religious leader has a responsibility to define the confusing issues in a social dilemma in terms of the revelation of God, the meaning of human sin, the availability of redemption, and the communion of the fellowship of believers in the church. Such a task is performed, at best, only in part, and must be accompanied by a confession of limited vision, an understanding of the conditions which formed the churchman's own attitude toward drink, and discussion so that God may bring forth new light about the complex problems of alcohol and alcoholism. Unless the church makes a serious and devout attempt to assimilate the facts for practical application, the information unearthed so far about alcohol and alcoholism will be of little value to the ministry.

The purpose, therefore, of this final chapter is to suggest a practical program for the care of alcoholics and the prevention of alcoholism in the context of the basic beliefs which Christians teach. The first basic belief focuses upon sin, the second explores redemption as it is related to alcohol and alcoholism, the third concerns the nature and purpose of the church and its ministry, the fourth relates the doctrine of God to the treatment of alcoholics.

Alcohol and the Doctrine of Sin

Churches of the frontier revival tradition have characteristically looked upon both the drinking of alcohol and the disease of alcoholism as sin. Any doctrinal and practical approach, therefore, must come to grips with this basic attitude at the outset. That which a Christian community considers to be sin becomes the basis for exclusion from fellowship. Sin "cuts off," estranges, alienates, and isolates. A Christian community's definition of sin determines the nature and basis of the fellowship among its members. We as churchmen, therefore, need to be sure that our beliefs reflect the mind of God as revealed in Jesus Christ rather than merely our own history.

Representatives of the frontier revival tradition, such as the Baptists of the South, were among those explorers who opened up the territories beyond the Alleghenies. The great grain-producing states found it easier to turn their crops into spirits than to transport corn by crude means of transportation. In Kentucky, for example, alcohol production became a business of international proportions. The formula for bourbon whiskey was invented by a Baptist minister near Georgetown, Kentucky, in the late 1700s.

Mass distribution and recent advertisement have made alcohol more available to the poor, more widely used by all social classes, and more deadly in its effects. Therefore, the Southern minister who lives in a community where distilleries form a large part of the economy is caught in a severe dilemma. While defining the use of alcohol as a personal sin to the individuals to whom he preaches, he knows that the local economy (hence the church itself) depends directly or indirectly on the alcohol industry.

In view of their strong emphasis on separation of church and state, Baptists in particular find themselves in another dilemma. Since the Civil War, they have been involved in the battle for legal prohibition. For a period of time, a Baptist minister may become involved on almost a full-time basis in urging a local option election to outlaw liquor. The same minister will refuse to participate in other controversial political movements on the grounds of separation of church and state. A pastor (or layman) may say—regarding race relations, for example—that the cultural habits of people cannot be changed by legislation. But he may be the first to insist on legislative control of alcohol.

The United States today is in the midst of great social changes. Many young people have educational and economic opportunities far beyond those of their parents. As they become more educated, they move from the lower or lower-middle class into the upper-middle or lower-upper class. We have seen that drinking as social behavior increases with the amount of education that people have. Therefore, ministers and lay people in the churches are faced with another contradictory situation. They encourage their young people "to get an education and to make something out of themselves." At the same time, the education itself either neutralizes or converts the attitude of the young person toward drinking. Even among older church members, of course, there are homes where alcohol is part of family rituals and festive occasions. Here social drinking is quietly approved though not publicly announced. Such families go to church and say together a covenant which was written during the struggle to make the use and sale of alcohol a criminal offense. Young persons, naturally enough, are bothered by the ambiguity.

In the presence of these dilemmas, the church as a community becomes so confused about alcohol and alcoholism that it loses both a clear sense of direction and a deep sense of integrity. In the face of this loss of direction and integrity, ministers and a few people in the church redouble their efforts. This produces a hard fanaticism against every shape, form, and fashion of alcohol —an attitude I have chosen to nickname "the-devil-in-a-bottle" understanding of sin in relation to alcohol and alcoholism. Here the church and its ministers seek to eliminate alcohol and alcoholism by blaming all evils on alcohol and assuming that if alcohol itself can be annihilated, then the ills of the alcoholic will go away. This effort only enslaves mankind, making him a puppet of his environment, a defenseless child in the presence of the roaring lion, alcohol.

This conception of sin puts the church and its ministry in the role of a protecting mother. The person who drinks becomes a recalcitrant child who must alternately be protected and punished. It assumes that sin is ignorance and that if a person is properly taught about alcohol, he will not drink it. It assumes that sin is wholly voluntary and that the person who becomes addicted to alcohol "ought to know better" and certainly can do better if he will simply straighten up, fly right, and exert will power.

However, the alcoholic may have been taught from his crib "never to touch the stuff" and that to drink alcohol is the moral equivalent of adultery. He already knows better, and his rebellion from dependence upon mother and mothering church is kept in force by the use of alcohol.

The devastating, but unseen, effect of this projection of sin upon the bottle of alcohol itself, however, does not stop with the alcoholic himself. Its worst impact is upon the inner spiritual lives of the pastor, the deacons, the Sunday School teachers, and the totally abstaining members of the church generally. We are destined never to confess our own sins since alcohol itself, not we ourselves, is responsible for alcoholism. We, therefore, keep the outside of the cup clean with a full show of respectability and freedom from drink. However, the inside of the cup is never touched. We never examine our own involvement in sin. We think of the alcoholic as a man or woman of unclean lips. We carefully delete the fact that he lives in the midst of a people of unclean lips.

Therefore, a more biblically grounded and full-orbed view of sin that will involve our own confession must precede the healing of the alcoholic. The defensive "devil-in-a-bottle" conception of sin enables the family, the church, and the pastor to survive temporarily. This attitude is poignantly understandable in the family, culturally explainable in a church, and financially rewarding to a pastor. Before God, however, family, church, and pastor have joined with the powers of sin to make sin all the more sinful. They have bound heavy burdens, and not a finger do they lift to help bear the yoke.

Jesus' Definition of Sin

The teachings of Jesus put us in touch with a comprehensive understanding of sin which challenges our little legalisms with reference to alcohol and alcoholism:

And he called the people to him again, and said to them, "Hear me, all of you, and understand: there is nothing outside a man which by going into him can defile him; but the things which come out of a man are what defile him." And when he had entered the house, and left the people, his disciples asked him about the parable. And he said to them, "Then are you also without understanding? Do you not see that whatever goes into a man from outside cannot defile him, since it enters, not his heart but his stomach, and so passes on?" (Thus he declared all foods clean.) And he said, "What comes out of a man is what defiles a man. For from within, out of the heart of man, come evil thoughts, fornication, theft, murder, adultery, coveting, wickedness, deceit, licentiousness, envy, slander, pride, foolishness. All these evil things come from within, and they defile a man (Mark 7:14-23, RSV).

Furthermore, the apostle Paul gives us a "distributive" point of view with reference to our interpretation of sin in the context of the Christian fellowship:

> Brethren, if a man is overtaken in any trespass, you who are spiritual should restore him in a spirit of gentleness. Look to yourself, lest you too be tempted. Bear one another's burdens, and so fulfill the law of Christ. For if any one thinks he is something, when he is nothing, he deceives himself. But let each one test his own work, and then his reason to boast will be in himself alone and not in his neighbor. For each man will have to bear his own load (Gal. 6:1-5, RSV).

We cannot look upon the involuntary, compulsive power of alcohol in the life of the alcoholic merely as ignorance, stupidity, or hardheadedness. This is a shallow understanding of the power of compulsion in the life of anyone. Such legalism hardens the situation with reference to the alcoholic and actually contributes to his alcoholism. The apostle Paul describes clearly and accurately the internal situation of the alcoholic:

> For sin, finding opportunity in the commandment, deceived me and by it killed me. I do not understand my own actions. For I do not do what I want, but I do the very thing I hate. Now if I do what I do not want, . . . it is no longer I that do it, but sin which dwells within me. . . . So I find it to be a law that when I want to do right, evil lies close at hand. I see in my members another law at war with the law of my mind and making me captive to the law of sin which dwells in my members. Wretched man that I am! Who will deliver me from this body of death? (Rom. 7:11,15-16, 20-21,23-24, RSV).

These three teachings of the New Testament outline a creative attitude toward sin in relation to alcohol and alcoholism. This attitude has three dimensions to it. First, alcohol is a part of creation, and our task is to find God's intention for its use so that it can bless and not curse human life. God means all of his creations to consecrate and not desecrate life. Evil lies in the heart of man and not in the bottle. What comes out of the heart of man defiles him, not what enters his mouth.

Second, any approach to the alcoholic as a sinner must begin with a confession of our own faults. We must look to ourselves lest we also be tempted. The alcoholic has his own individual responsibility; each man shall bear his own burden. But there are corporate responsibilities as well. By bearing one another's burdens we fulfil the law of Christ. Therefore, we are to confess our faults one to another in order that not only the alcoholic but we ourselves may be healed.

We are a fellowship of sinners and not just a fellowship of the righteous. If we miss this we become so filled with our sense of being right that we are empty of the goodness which God intends. However, this cannot be a sentimental goodness, buttered over with sweet nothings that overindulge an alcoholic and protect him from his own responsibilities. It must be a hard-headed realism that shares and bears responsibility.

Third, this attitude toward sin involves an appreciation of the compulsive, irrational, violent nature of human beings. Even as the alcoholic becomes compulsively addicted to alcohol, so the overpious religious person can become addicted to self-righteousness and be lost in the power of his pride. He "prays thus within himself" and thanks God he is not as other men. Conversion to this kind of religion may free the person of alcohol, but it does not free him of omnipotent pride.

Furthermore, a religion of works can be a kind of addiction. There is such a thing as what I have chosen to nickname "workaholism." The "workaholic" trusts in his own works for redemption. He becomes addicted to busyness and tries to prove his omnipotence by attempting everything, being everywhere, and being all things to all men at all times. As for thinking of God as one who loves him whether he produces or not, this is unthinkable to the person addicted to work. Acceptance is pay for work done.

The alcoholic who is converted to legalistic religion may substitute this religion of works for his dependence upon alcohol. From the point of view of his productivity as a human being and the happiness of his family, none would deny that this is a much better social solution than drinking alcohol. However, from the point of view of the happiness and serenity of the new convert, much is desired in the way of freedom from the bondage, which a more nearly complete conversion would effect.

The church, the pastor, and the converted alcoholic who build their understanding of sin on the legalistic bases which have been rejected here tend to find themselves defeated in their attempts to minister to other alcoholics. Freedom from drink is equated with salvation, and it is unthinkable in such a view that a person who has once made a decision for Christ and fallen into drink again could possibly have any relationship to God. Therefore, a return to drink is tantamount to heresy, breaches the fellowship, and represents a backsliding from faith in God. This conception of backsliding is compatible with perfectionistic sects, but incompatible with the genuine kind of security that comes from ultimate trust in the forgiveness of God. This kind of salvation is a conditional salvation.

What Redemption Is

If the difficulty of the church's doctrine of sin is found in "the-devil-in-a-bottle" theory of sin, then the alcoholic's converse trouble is that he seeks his redemption in a bottle. He feels keenly the need for a god greater than himself but surrenders to the power of alcohol. He lacks center and heart to his purpose for living, and although he yearns to transcend himself and rise above his limitation, he does so through the temporary sense of omnipotence which alcohol gives him. Thus, he is trapped in the idolatry of alcohol itself. In return, alcohol gives him a counterfeit sense of dependence, a false sense of security, and an unreal sense of power. In other words, he looks to alcohol for redemption from the burden of his humanity, the power of his guilt, the threat of his insecurity.

The search for God in the power of alcohol is the antithesis of surrender—either as an act or as a state of existence—and forms the stuff of which the alcoholic's addiction is made psychologically. He fancies that he can at any time quit drinking if he so chooses. He imagines that he is unique and completely different from other people, both in his sense of guilt and his sense of power. He firmly holds out against any dependence upon anyone else when he is in a remotely sober state. His feelings of total independence take over while he is sober, and the utter reality of dependence breaks through when he is blacked out with alcohol. Through the instrument of alcohol, the alcoholic becomes "dead weight" on his family and the community, both of whom reject him.

The practical approach of church people to the alcoholic quite often fails because the same pride and self-sufficiency which characterizes an alcoholic when he is relatively sober pervades the attitudes of religious people toward their own religious respectability. These forms of pride collide with the pride of the alcoholic. The end result is a stalemate, and the tyranny of the separate forms of pride prevents either the alcoholic or the religious person from admitting his need for the other, his need for forgiveness, or his need for God.

A Practical Approach

A more fruitful and productive practical approach to the alcoholic on the part of religious people, therefore, would be an invitation to fellowship in the confession of faults and sin. The individual pastor, for example, in talking with an alcoholic, can say: "Whereas you are in the power of alcohol, struggling to become free, I am in the power of impatience and a sharp, brittle temper, struggling to be free. I know what it is to be weaker than my desires." This comes as strange news to the alcoholic. The strange news may even turn into good news when he discovers further that he is not alone in his weakness.

Another possible ground of communication is established with the alcoholic when a small and intimate group of people whom he knows personally are willing to have him visit in their homes as a friend. A meal shared with him and his wife—both of whom long since have quit the company of others as a couple—can be a simple communion of acceptance in the face of the known fact that he drinks too much. However, this mutual burden-bearing cannot be of the kind that treats the alcoholic as a child, removes responsibility for his own behavior from him, and protects him from the consequences of his mistakes. To the contrary, the creation of a steadfast relationship that makes room for his weakness as a drinker, and is not conditioned on his drinking or not drinking, is a necessary prelude to his actually meeting the unmerited grace of God in Jesus Christ. It is in the matter-of-fact acceptance by a few Christians that he begins dimly to realize that "there is therefore now no condemnation for those who are in Christ Jesus. For the law of the Spirit of life in Christ Jesus has set me free from the law of sin" (Rom. 8:1-2, RSV).

Redemption in Jesus Christ makes itself known to an alcoholic through the realistic love of a small, face-to-face, homelike fellowship of a few other Christians who are of one mind toward the alcoholic helplessly trapped in addiction. Christ comes as a friend and a helper to those who are powerless to help themselves. The Christian does not require any promises of the alcoholic, particularly the promise not to drink again. This is not the covenant that binds the Christian together with the alcoholic. If it were, the act of drinking would have the power to cancel the unconditional love of Jesus Christ. Therefore, the covenant of the Christian is to love the alcoholic as Christ has loved him and given himself for him. This the alcoholic cannot do without the help of the Holy Spirit, who "helps us in our weakness; for we do not know how to pray as we ought, but the Spirit himself intercedes for us with sighs too deep for words" (Rom. 8:26, RSV).

If, in Jesus Christ, death, life, angels, principalities, things present, things to come, powers, height, depth are all powerless to separate us from the love of God in Christ Jesus, is it then difficult to believe that alcohol cannot separate us from the love of God in Christ Jesus, either?

The pastor symbolizes the "communion of the concerned" as well as the overpowering demands of the conscience. Thus, he may be called upon for help at any hour by the distressed family and the remorse-ridden alcoholic. He is hard put to know what to do in this extreme situation. What are some simple, specific methods for dealing with an alcoholic under these circumstances?

The pastor should inspect the situation carefully by telephone before leaving the house. If the alcoholic or members of his family are in personal danger, hospitalization may be necessary. He may ask the alcoholic to meet him at the emergency room of a local hospital where medication and treatment for acute alcoholization can be started. A physician may be there or the family physician can be called at the same time, either by the family or by the pastor with the family's permission. If the family is penniless, a public hospital can often help on an emergency basis.

Longer range planning needs to be made within the church, too, so that the pastor can have a trained group of church members give teamwork assistance in such emergencies. Standard procedures can be established whereby three or four laymen and women can quietly and anonymously become a working group for assisting the pastor in the routine handling of alcoholic crises. Concentrated time spent training medical, institutional, and lay people to work together on such crises will pay long-run dividends in the day-to-day assistance given alcoholics and their families on such occasions.[1]

The Role of the Church

An understanding of sin and redemption as defined in preceding chapters ought to create real questions as to the purpose of the church and its ministry.

The statistical and clinical data presented earlier in this book have underscored the way in which the Jewish faith, particularly

---

[1]An excellent guide for such a training program is *Alcoholism: A Guide for the Clergy,* published by the National Council on Alcoholism, 2 East 103rd Street, New York, New York, 10029.

in its orthodox expression, has produced a religious community in which low-content alcoholic beverages are used ceremonially and symbolically as an expression of the community of faith and love. Furthermore, the large part played by the home in the teaching of the Jewish faith includes family rituals, symbols, holy days, and holidays for the sustenance of the individual members in intimate family fellowship. This fellowship nourishes the vertical dimension in its worship of God, whom the Jewish father represents but never replaces.

In the early church, as depicted in the book of Acts and the letters of Paul, the "church-in-thy-house" was the principle expression of the Christian fellowship. Beyond this there were only the synagogues in which to meet. The ceremonial meal of the Lord's Supper, according to competent New Testament scholars such as Professor Frank Stagg, was one of the earliest community-symbolic expressions of the death, burial, and resurrection of Jesus Christ as the Lord.

Today alcoholism is highest among those religious groups where this "church-in-thy-house" has perished. The unstructured, spontaneous, and uninhibited sharing of spiritual conversation, food and drink, and noncompetitive acceptance of one another has given way to such superficialities as receptions, teas, and cocktail parties devoid of distinct religious meaning, high tradition, and profound fellowship. Rather, these occasions are saturated with evidences of pretense, feelings of comparison, and competitive needs to impress. The tavern becomes an honest place by comparison.

Therefore, my first recommendation to churches for the care of alcoholics and the prevention of alcoholism would be a rediscovery of the role of the father in the Christian home as one who energizes its religious life. In turn, the large, highly organized meetings of the church need to be revivified by small religious gatherings of adults in one another's homes without trappings of secularized social rituals. The fact that a considerable number of active church members "need" to participate in cocktail parties in the homes is a perversion of the need for the "church-in-thy-house" and evidence that we have too much temple religion and not enough time for the free, informal, spontaneous meeting of Christians in the home.

Many contemporary psychologists, principally Erik Erikson, have emphasized that the young adult is ready for intimacy with other young adults and needs the solidarity of close affiliation. The counterpart of this intimacy is what Erikson calls "distantiation." The very mass structure of our wholesale approach to religion can contribute to, rather than offset, this distantiation. For the person struggling with the isolation characteristic of the alcoholic, the public situation of worship is in itself a terror-producing experience. To demand that a person struggling with the overpowering force of alcohol make a "public profession" is to create in him a need for alcohol to anesthetize the terror that such an experience involves.

The church should profit from the experience of Alcoholics Anonymous and provide one or two, and not more than three, faithful and trustworthy friends for an alcoholic and/or his family. Low flame interest should be shown the family and the alcoholic without demands for decisions, attendance at public meetings, and so on.

These two or three friends can extend the ministries of their families to the alcoholic and his family. If meetings at the church are to be attended, they should be small group meetings and not too much attention should be called to the presence of the alcoholic. However, in "aftermeetings," individual expressions of attention can be very helpful. In no instance should the alcoholic be used as a public example either of drunkenness or sobriety. This contributes to, and does not resolve, his problem of drink. It creates the stress which alcohol originally began relieving and preconditions the alcoholic's return to drinking.

One pastor recounts the story of an alcoholic in his church who was converted and made a profession of faith on a Sunday evening. He received continuing pastoral care, attention from a

group of friends in the church, and was enabled to maintain
sobriety for a period of six months. The annual revival time
came. He was asked by some of his friends to give his testimony
at one of the evening services of the revival. It was announced
ahead of time. The church was packed with people. When the
time came for him to give him testimony, the man was sufficiently
drunk to be able only to start and not to finish his testimony.
This is the kind of terror-producing situation which called for
alcohol-induced courage. Any experienced speaker who has been
trained in facing crowds knows what courage it requires. Even
people not disabled by alcoholism are terrified by public speaking. Yet we, with insensitivity, try to prod those recently free of
drink onto the platform! It should never be done.

The alcoholic is helped most by being allowed to make his
profession of faith to a small company of those whom he knows
well and who are able to vouch for him at an evening service or
at a small gathering of the fellowship of believers. After such a
profession of faith, he should have a continuing "sponsor" who
serves as a confidant to whom he can unburden his many personal
difficulties. This confidant should be a person of patience who
requires no "works of merit" of the alcoholic; he offers his friendship and his confidence but requires nothing in return.

The Church and Therapy

The acute or chronic alcoholic, however, needs specialized
therapy. The Christian church and its ministry can provide
context, compassion, and commitment for the alcoholic. In both
the acute and chronic phases of alcoholism, however, this context,
compassion, and commitment must take specialized therapeutic
forms. These forms are specifically as follows:

First, the alcoholic needs medical attention. The dietary,
poisonous, and exposure side effects of alcohol can kill an alcoholic. The pious assumption that the alcoholic cannot be helped
unless he is sober and unless he wants aid can result in the
church's neglecting to get medical care for a person in danger

of death. The family physician should be called either by the family or by some representative of the church. Hospitalization may or may not be indicated. Treatment of alcohol intoxication is aimed at getting the patient sober as quickly and painlessly as possible, discovering any medical or psychiatric complications, and trying to get the patient to feel the need for continuing help. Glucose containing Vitamin B complex, injections of other vitamin supplements, the use of clinically validated drugs, and enforced sleep—all are steps that doctors may take.

To get at the immediate situation of alcohol intoxication may require from three to four days. Longer term treatment involves such problems as getting the alcoholic to accept the diagnosis of alcoholism and to agree to follow the treatment. As Jackson A. Smith says, this may mean to the alcoholic "the loss of the very glue with which he is stuck together."

However, the keystone of the long-term rehabilitation of an alcoholic is the establishment of a continuing, durable, and trustworthy relationship between the alcoholic and a person or small group "whose approval he learns to consider most worthwhile." It has been said that the alcoholic is a sick man or woman for whom institutionalization is indicated but for whom no adequate institution has been devised. The local denominational hospitals scattered over our country can give short-term medical help to alcoholics. This kind of medical help has already been described. However, in spite of the tremendous investments in money, personnel, and equipment, Protestant hospitals are not equipped to give rehabilitative care to alcoholics.

The final and most imperative suggestion to be made in this book for the care of alcoholics, therefore, is an appeal to all Protestant groups to begin to invest a fraction of the money spent on hospitals and temperance efforts in a few rehabilitation centers for alcoholics. These rehabilitation centers should combine the following features:

1. Specialized medical and nursing care with tailored medical procedures for treating the immediate effects of alcohol intoxica-

tion. Longer term psychological and psychiatric help should be provided.

2. Specialized social casework attention with trained social workers equipped to counsel with all of the family members of the alcoholic.

3. A work program which combines intrainstitutional work, supervised by occupational therapists, with extrainstitutional work, which gives more responsibility to the alcoholic as he is ready to accept it. Vocational recovery and rehabilitation, with special attention to the meaninglessness characteristic of many alcoholics' lives and jobs, should be a main concern of such a center.

4. Small group work with two specific kinds of groups between which the alcoholic is free to choose: (1) a specifically non-religious group in which no religious commitment or concern is expected, required, or provided; (2) a distinctly religious group in which the resources of Bible study, prayer, and religious conversation are definitely provided. There should be freedom to move from one group to the other as long as the person himself chooses and explains to the group leader that he is changing.

5. Active cooperation with Alcoholics Anonymous, with AA members providing leadership according to their own design.

6. Individual pastoral counseling provided by a clinically trained chaplain who serves as the administrator and integrator of the program outlined above. Ministers in training in the care of the alcoholic could be individual counselors under the supervision of such a director of the rehabilitation center.

The Christian community needs to experiment in new forms of its own spiritual outreach in order to meet the specialized needs of alcoholics. It has demonstrated its ability to do so in the ministry to deprived children, the aged, the physically ill, and to a less extent with the mentally ill. The objective of such a community should become what it is in the training of the ministry, that the alcoholic should become a person "thoroughly furnished to every good work" in the Christian faith. Such a community should be closely related, preferably to a given local church, but should be sustained and supported by the denomination as a whole.

For All Have Sinned

The hopeless struggle between the total abstainer's "devil-in-a-bottle" attitude toward the alcoholic and the alcoholic's feverish search for "God-in-a-bottle" is a deadlock. When the pious church member and the stubborn alcoholic call for the capitulation of each other, the total situation deteriorates. The conventional churchman holds out the forms of religion as a price that the alcoholic must pay for his redemption. This situation crudely ignores the personal feelings involved in sin and redemption, and leaves both churchman and alcoholic as spectators on the sidelines, uninvolved and not responsible for the total situation.

The churchman and the alcoholic need to see themselves as persons responsible for making ethical decisions. Recognition of the personal factor will require empathy and confession of sin on the part of pastor and people.

God confronts us in Jesus Christ as neither detached from us nor requiring us to be omnipotent and perfect. Rather, he encounters us as the God-man, divine in his power to forgive and human in his power to feel our infirmities.

God in Christ is always opposed to both the self-sufficient claims of the alcoholic and the self-righteous pretenses of the pious. Both the self-sufficiency of the alcoholic and the self-righteousness of the pious are attempts to supplant God. God is always at work bringing to despair those who would supplant him. He brings to naught both the self-chosen loneliness of the alcoholic and the exclusiveness of church members who are too good to associate with winebibbers and gluttons. He leads us into a wilderness of moral confusion, bringing us as he did Jacob to the wrestling despair of the river Jabbok. Like Jacob we are required of God to remain in this despair until we seek the blessing and relief of God.

The alcoholic begins the road to recovery by admitting that he is powerless to help himself. He will walk all his life with the limp of his propensity to drink as a reminder of his need for redemption. The churchman who has admitted to an alcoholic his own frailties as a sinner carries his own confession of sin as a reminder that he too can be tempted and needs God. As they acknowledge their imperfections, the Perfect One visits them in the power of the Holy Spirit to heal them as fellow sinners, reliant upon Jesus Christ for temporal health and eternal hope.

Bibliography

Alcoholics Anonymous: The Story of How Many Thousands of Men and Women Have Recovered from Alcoholism. New and rev. ed. New York: Alcoholics Anonymous Publishing, 1955.

American Medical Association Committee on Alcoholism. "Hospitalization of Patients with Alcoholism" (Reports of Officers), *Journal of the American Medical Association,* CLXII (1956), 750.

ANDERSON, D. "Alcohol and Public Opinion," *Quarterly Journal of Studies on Alcohol,* III (1942), 376-92.

Annals of the American Academy of Political Social Science, CCCXV (1958).

BIER, W. C. (ed.). *Problems in Addiction: Alcoholism and Narcotics.* New York: Fordham University Press, 1962.

BRUNNER-ORNE, M. and ORNE, M. T. "Directive Group-Therapy in the Treatment of Alcoholics: Technique and Rationale," *International Journal on Group Psychotherapy,* IV (1954), 293-302.

CARLSON, A. J. "The Conditioned-Reflex Therapy of Alcohol Addiction," *Quarterly Journal of Studies on Alcohol,* V (1944), 212-15.

CLINEBELL, H. J., JR. *Understanding and Counseling the Alcoholic Through Religion and Psychology.* Nashville: Abingdon Press, 1956.

CONGER, J. J. "Reinforcement Theory and the Dynamics of Alcoholism," *Quarterly Journal of Studies on Alcohol,* XVII (1956), 296-305.

133

DIETHELM, O. (ed.). *Etiology of Chronic Alcoholism.* Springfield, Ill.: Thomas, 1955.

EFRON, VERA, and KELLER, MARK. *Selected Statistical Tables on the Consumption of Alcohol, 1950-1962, and on Alcoholism.* New Brunswick, N. J.: Journal of Studies on Alcohol, 1963.

ERIKSON, ERIK. *Identity and the Life Cycle.* New York: International Universities Press, 1959.

FALLDING, HAROLD. "The Source and Burden of Civilization Illustrated in the Use of Alcohol," *Quarterly Journal of Studies on Alcohol,* XXV, No. 4 (1964), 714-24.

FLEMING, R. "The Treatment of Chronic Alcoholism," *New English Journal of Medicine,* CCXVII (1937), 779-83.

———. "On Certain Medical Aspects of Alcoholism," *Bulletin of the Academy of Medicine of New Jersey,* I, No. 3 (1956).

HOCH, P. H. Quoted by Kruse, H. D. (ed.). *Alcoholism as a Medical Problem.* New York: Hoeber-Harper, 1956.

ISBELL, H. "Craving for Alcohol," *Quarterly Journal of Studies on Alcohol,* XVI (1955), 38-42.

JACKSON, JOAN. "The Adjustment of the Family to the Crisis of Alcoholism," *Quarterly Journal of Studies on Alcohol,* XV, No. 4 (1954), 562-86.

JACO, E. GARTLY, *The Social Epidemiology of Mental Disorders.* New York: Russell Sage Foundation, 1960.

JELLINEK, E. M. *The Disease Concept of Alcoholism.* New Haven: College and University Press, 1960.

———. "Phases of Alcohol Addiction," *Quarterly Journal of Studies on Alcohol,* XIII (1952), 673-84.

———. "The Problems of Alcohol," *Alcohol, Science, and Society.* New Haven, Conn.: Quarterly Journal of Studies on Alcohol, 1945. Cf. pp. 13-29.

JONES, HOWARD. *Alcoholic Addiction.* London: Tavistock, 1963.

KELLER, MARK, and SEELEY, J. R. *The Alcohol Language.* Toronto: The University of Toronto Press, 1958.

LAKE, R. "Twelve Steps for Alcoholics," *Today's Health,* XXXV (November, 1957), 18-19, *passim.*

LOLLI, GIORGIO. "Alcoholism, 1941-1951; A Survey of Activities in Research, Education, and Therapy. Part V: The Treatment of Alcohol Addiction," *Quarterly Journal of Studies on Alcohol,* XIII (1952), 461-71.

————. "Alcoholism and Obesity, Both Problems of Hunger," *Connecticut Review of Alcoholism,* V (1953), 1, 3-4.

————. "Alcoholism As a Disorder of the Love Disposition," *Quarterly Journal of Studies on Alcohol,* XVII (1956), 96-107.

————. "Alcoholism As a Medical Problem," *Bulletin of the New York Academy of Medicine,* XXXI (1955), 876-85.

McCARTHY, RAYMOND F. *Teenagers and Alcohol.* New Haven: Yale Center of Alcohol Studies, 1956.

McPEEK, F. W. "Alcoholism and Religion," *Social Action,* XVI, No. 4 (1950), 4-29.

MANN, M. *Primer on Alcoholism.* New York: Rinehart, 1950.

MULFORD, H. A. "Drinking and Deviant Drinking, U.S.A., 1963," *Quarterly Journal of Studies on Alcohol,* XXV, No. 4 (1964), 634-50.

"New Statement on Alcoholic Beverages by the General Assembly of the Presbyterian Church in the U.S.A." ("Current Notes"), *Quarterly Journal of Studies on Alcohol,* VII (1946), 121-25.

PITTMAN, DAVID, and SNYDER, CHARLES R. (eds.). *Society, Culture, and Drinking Patterns.* New York: John Wiley and Sons, 1962.

Protestant Episcopal Church in the United States of America, Joint Commission on Alcoholism. *Alcohol, Alcoholism, and Social Drinking.* Greenwich, Conn.: Seabury Press, 1958.

RICE, O. R. "The Contribution of the Minister to the Treatment of the Alcoholic," *Quarterly Journal of Studies on Alcohol,* V (1944), 250-56.

SESSIONS, PERCY M. "Ego Religion and Superego Religion in Alcoholics," *Quarterly Journal of Studies on Alcohol,* XVIII (1957), 121-25.

SMITH, JACKSON A. "Problems in the Treatment of the Alcoholic," *Quarterly Journal of Studies on Alcohol,* Supplement 1 (November, 1961).

STRAUS, R., and BACON, S. D. *Drinking in College.* New Haven: Yale University Press, 1953.

TIEBOUT, H. M. "The Act of Surrender in the Therapeutic Process With Special Reference to Alcoholism," *Quarterly Journal of Studies on Alcohol,* X (1949), 48-58.

————. "Alcoholics Anonymous: An Experiment of Nature,"

Quarterly Journal of Studies on Alcohol, XXII (1961), 62-68.
————. "Conversion as a Psychological Phenomena (in the Treatment of the Alcoholic)," *Pastoral Psychology,* II, No. 13 (1951), 28-34.
————. "Surrender Versus Compliance," *Pastoral Psychology,* IX (1958), 25-33.
————, "The Ego Factors in Surrender in Alcoholism," *Quarterly Journal of Studies on Alcohol,* XV (1954), 610-21.
ULLMAN, A. D. "Sociocultural Backgrounds of Alcoholism," *Annals of the American Academy of Political Social Science,* CCCXV (1958), 48-54.
WHALEN, THELMA. "Wives of Alcoholics: Four Types Observed in a Family Service Agency," *Quarterly Journal of Studies on Alcohol,* XIV (1953), 632-41.
WILLIAMS, R. J. *Nutrition and Alcoholism.* Norman, Okla.: University of Oklahoma Press, 1951.
————. *The Nutritional Approach.* Austin: University of Texas Press, 1959.
World Health Organization. Expert Committee on Mental Health. Report of the First Session of the Alcoholism Subcommittee. (W. H. O. Technical Report Series, No. 42.) Geneva, 1951.
————. Expert Committee on Drugs Liable to Produce Addiction. Third Report. (W.H.O. Technical Report Series, No. 57.) Geneva, 1952.
————. Expert Committee on Alcohol. First Report. (W.H.O. Technical Report Series, No. 84.) Geneva, 1954.
————. *Alcohol and Alcoholism.* Report of an Expert Committee. (W.H.O. Technical Report Series, No. 94.) Geneva, 1955.